THIS BOOK BELONGS TO

I made an umbrella and covered it with skins (page 76)

I gave him something to eat and drink (page 113)

ROBINSON CRUSOE

ROBINSON CRUSOE

by Daniel Defoe

Bounty Books

First published in 1990 by Ward Lock Limited

This edition published 2005 by Bounty Books,
a division of Octopus Publishing Group Ltd,
2-4 Heron Quays, London E14 4JP

Copyright © 2005 Octopus Publishing Group Ltd

ISBN-13   9780753712313
ISBN   0 7573 1231 8

Printed and bound in Slovenia

LIST OF ILLUSTRATIONS

CONTENTS

PREFACE

Daniel Defoe, the author of *Robinson Crusoe*, was born in London in 1660 or 1661. His father wanted him to be a minister, but he was adventurous in nature and liked to travel, although he often got into trouble. In the book, Robinson Crusoe blames himself for this and shows how much happiness it cost him.

Defoe took part in the Duke of Monmouth's rebellion to gain the throne of England from James II, and narrowly escaped being hanged. He was always writing on problems of the day, and was against cruelty and wrong. But he suffered for such writings.

Next to *Robinson Crusoe*, Defoe's best-known novel is *A Journal of the Plague Year*, a story about the terrible epidemic of 1665. *Robinson Crusoe*, too, was based on a true story about Alexander Selkirk, a seaman who spent eight months all alone on the island of Juan Fernandez off the coast of Chile. He made a coat and hat of goatskins, using a nail as a needle; started a fire by rubbing two sticks together; and behaved like the hero of this book in many other ways.

Robinson Crusoe was first published in 1719 and has continued to be issued ever since. Although many stories of adventure have been written like it, this book still has a special place in the literature of the world.

CHAPTER ONE

CRUSOE RUNS AWAY TO SEA

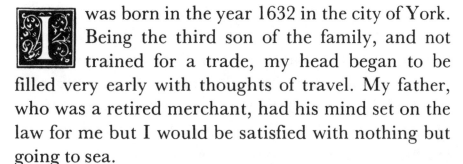was born in the year 1632 in the city of York. Being the third son of the family, and not trained for a trade, my head began to be filled very early with thoughts of travel. My father, who was a retired merchant, had his mind set on the law for me but I would be satisfied with nothing but going to sea.

My father one day gave me serious and excellent counsel against what he could see was my plan.

I was sincerely affected with this discourse and I resolved not to think of going abroad. But alas! My resolve wore off in a few days and, to prevent any of my father's further importunities, a few weeks later I decided to run far away from him.

It was not till almost a year after this that I broke loose. But being one day at Hull, whither I went casually and without any purpose of running away at that time, and one of my companions then going to London by sea in his father's ship and urging me to go with them, I consulted neither father nor mother, nor so much as sent them word of my doing this, but left them to hear of it as they might, without asking God's blessing, or my father's, without any consideration of circumstances or consequences, and in an ill hour, God knows.

On the 1st September, 1651, I went on board. The ship had no sooner got out of the Humber than the wind began to blow and the waves to rise in a most frightful manner; and as I had never been at sea before, I was most inexpressibly sick in body and terrified in mind. I began now seriously to reflect upon what I had done, and how justly I was overtaken by the judgment of heaven for wickedly leaving my father's house.

All this while the storm increased and the sea, which I had never been upon before, went very high, though nothing like what I have seen many times since. I expected every wave would swallow us up, and in this agony of mind, I made many vows and resolutions that if it would please God to spare my life this voyage, I would go directly home to my father and never set foot on a ship again while I lived; that I would take his advice and never run myself into such miseries as these any more.

These wise and sober thoughts continued during the storm, and indeed some time after; but the next day, as the wind abated and the sea grew calmer, I began to grow a little used to it. However, I was very grave that day, being also a little seasick still; but towards night, the weather cleared up, the wind was down, and a charming, fine evening followed. The sun went down in clear weather and rose so the next morning. With little or no wind and a smooth sea, and with the sun shining upon it, I thought the sight was the most delightful that I ever saw.

I had slept well in the night and was no longer seasick, but very cheerful. And, alas, with my miseries had gone all my repentance, all my reflections upon my past conduct, and all my resolutions about going home.

The sixth day at sea we came into Yarmouth Roads, for the wind having been contrary and the weather calm, we had made but little way since the storm. Here we were obliged to come to an anchor, and here we lay, the wind continuing contrary, that is, at southwest, for seven or eight days. On the eighth day in the morning, the wind increased and we had all hands at work to strike our topmasts and make everything snug and close, that the ship might ride as easy as possible. By noon the sea went very high indeed, and by nightfall our ship rode forecastle in, shipped several seas, and we thought once or twice our anchor had come home and we were doomed.

By this time it blew a terrible storm indeed, and now I began to see terror and amazement in the faces of even the seamen themselves. In the middle of the night, one of the men roused me and told me that we had sprung a leak, that there was four feet of water in the hold, and that I, who was able to do nothing before, was as well able to pump as another. At this I stirred myself and went to the pump and worked very heartily. Meanwhile, the master ordered us to fire a gun as a signal of distress. I, who had no idea what that meant, was so surprised that I fell down in a swoon. As this was a time when everybody had his own life to think of, no one noticed me or what had happened to me. Another man stepped up to the pump, and thrusting me aside with his foot, let me lie, thinking I had been killed. It was a long time, then, before I came to myself.

We worked on but the water increased in the hold and it was apparent that the ship would founder. So the master continued firing guns for help and a light ship just ahead of us ventured to send a boat out to help us. It was only by putting themselves in great danger that they took us off.

It was no use for them or us, after we were in the boat, to think of reaching their own ship, so all agreed to let her drive, and only to pull her in toward shore as much as we could; and our master promised them that, if the boat broke up on the shore, he would make it good to their master. So partly rowing and partly driving, our boat went away to the northward, sloping toward the shore almost as far as Winterton-Ness.

We were not much more than a quarter of an hour out of our ship when we saw her sink.

While the men were still pulling at the oar to bring the boat near the shore, we could see (when, our boat mounting the waves, we were able to see the shore) a great many people running along the strand to assist us when we should come near. However, we made very slow progress toward the shore, and were not able to reach it till, being past the lighthouse at Winterton, the shore falls off to the westward near Cromer, so that the land sheltered us a little from the violence of the wind. Here we got in and, though not without much difficulty, got all safely on shore, and walked afterward on foot to Yarmouth. There, as unfortunate men, we were treated with great humanity, both by the magistrates of the town, who assigned us good quarters, as by the particular merchants and owners of ships. We were given sufficient money to pay our way either to London or back to Hull, whichever we might choose.

As to going home, it immediately occurred to me how I would be laughed at by everybody, and how ashamed I would be to see my mother and father and all the others. So I went on board a vessel bound for the coast of Africa, or as the sailors vulgarly call it, a Voyage to Guinea.

It was my lot, first of all, to fall into pretty good company in London. I became acquainted with a ship's master, who had been on the coast of Guinea and who, having had very good success there, was resolved to go again. He, taking a fancy to my conversation, told me that if I would go that voyage with him, I would be his messmate and his companion; and if I could carry anything to sell along with me, I would have all the advantage of it the trade would admit.

I embraced the offer and went the voyage with him, and, through the honesty and good advice of my friend the captain, I succeeded in trade and increased my small investment greatly. For I carried about forty pounds in such toys and trifles as the captain directed me to buy. This forty pounds I mustered together by the assistance of some of my relatives whom I corresponded with and who, I believe, got my father or my mother to contribute that amount to my first adventure. This voyage made me both a sailor and a merchant, for I brought home five pounds nine ounces of gold dust as a result of my trade, which yielded me in London, on my return, almost three hundred pounds.

CHAPTER TWO

THE ESCAPE FROM THE MOORS

 was now set up as a Guinea trader, and though my friend, to my great misfortune, died soon after our return, I resolved to go the same voyage again.

I embarked in the same vessel with one who was his mate in the former voyage, and had now taken the command of the ship. I carried only one hundred pounds of my new-gained capital, the balance being lodged with my friend's widow. Sailing between the Canary Islands and the African shore, we were surprised, in the dawn of the morning, by a Turkish vessel whose captain gave chase to us with all the sail his ship could make.

About three in the afternoon he came up with us and, by mistake, brought to just athwart our quarter instead of athwart our stern, as he intended. We brought eight of our guns to bear on that side and poured in a broadside upon him, which made him sheer off again after returning our fire, and also pouring in his small shot from near two hundred men

I went to the pump and worked very heartily (page 14)

A Turkish vessel gave chase to us (page 18)

whom he had on board to defend his vessel.

However, we had not a man touched, all our men keeping close rank. Laying us on board the next time upon our other quarter, he entered sixty men upon our decks, who immediately fell to cutting and hacking the sails and rigging. We plied them with small shot, half-pikes, powder chests and such like, and cleared our decks of them twice.

However, to cut short this melancholy part of our story, our ship was disabled and three of our men killed, and eight wounded, so we were obliged to yield, and were all carried off as prisoners into Sallé, a port belonging to the Moors.

The treatment I had there was not as dreadful as I feared it might be. I was not taken up the country to the emperor's court, as the rest of our men were, but was kept by the captain of the rover as his proper prize and made his slave, being young and nimble and fit.

After about two years, an odd circumstance presented itself, which put the old thought of making some attempt for my liberty into my head. My patron was staying at home longer than usual without fitting out his ship, which, I heard, was for want of money. He used constantly to take the long boat of our English ship, on which he had built a little stateroom or cabin, and go fishing out into the waters.

He always took me and a young Moresco with him, and I became very dextrous in catching fish, so much so that sometimes he would send me with a Moor, one of his kinsmen, and the Moresco youth to catch a dish of fish for him. It happened that he had appointed to go out in this boat with two or three distinguished Moors, and had therefore sent on board the boat, overnight, a larger stock of provisions than ordinary and had ordered me to get ready three fusees, with powder and shot, because they planned to do some fowling as well as fishing.

I got all things ready as he directed. However, by and by my patron came on board alone, and told me his guests had put off going. He then ordered me, with a man and a boy called Xury, to go out with the boat and catch him some fish as usual.

Notions of escape at once darted into my thoughts, for now I found I was to have a little ship at my command. So, my master being gone, I prepared to furnish myself, not for a fishing trip, but for a different kind of voyage.

I first contrived to get the kinsman to bring on board some food supplies. This I managed to do by playing on manners. I told him we must not presume to eat of our patron's bread. He said that was true, so he brought a large basket of rusk or biscuit of their kind, and three jars of fresh water into the boat. I conveyed a great lump of beeswax into the boat, which weighed about half a hundredweight, and also a parcel of twine, a hatchet, a saw, and a hammer, all of which were of great use to us afterward, especially the wax to make candles. Thus furnished with much of what we needed, we sailed out of port under the pretext of going to fish.

After we had fished some time and caught nothing (for, when I had fish on my hook, I would not pull them up, so he could not see them), I said to the Moor:

"This will not do; our master will not be served thus; we must stand farther off." He agreed, and being at the head of the boat, set the sails; and as I had the helm, I ran the boat near a league farther and then brought to, as if I would fish. Then, giving the boy the helm, I stepped forward to where the Moor was, and I took him by surprise. With my arm under his waist, I tossed him overboard into the sea. He rose immediately and swam for the shore, and I have no doubt that he reached it with ease, for he was an excellent swimmer.

I then turned to the boy and said,

"Xury, if you will be faithful to me, I will make you a great man, but if you will not swear allegiance, I must throw you into the sea too." The boy swore to be faithful to me and to go all over the world with me.

While I was in view of the Moor who was swimming, I stood out directly to sea with the boat, rather stretching to windward, so they would think I was going toward the Straits.

But as soon as it grew dusk in the evening, I changed my course and steered directly south and by east, bending my course a little toward the east so that I might keep in with the shore; and having a fair fresh gale of wind, and a smooth quiet sea, I made such sail that I believe by the next day, at three o'clock in the afternoon, when I made the land, I could not be less than one hundred and fifty miles south of Sallé, quite beyond the Emperor of Morocco's dominions, or indeed of any other king thereabout, for we saw no people.

As I had been to this coast once before, I knew very well that the islands of the Canaries, and the Cape Verde Islands also, lay not far from the coast that loomed ahead.

Once or twice, in the daytime, I thought I saw the Pico of Tenerife, being the top of the mountain Tenerife, in the Canaries, and had a great mind to venture out in hopes of reaching thither. But, having tried twice, I was forced in again by contrary winds. Also the sea was too high for my little vessel, so I resolved to pursue my first design and keep along the shore.

After this stop, we headed southward continually for ten or twelve days, living very sparingly on our provisions, which were disappearing rapidly, and going no oftener into shore than we were obliged to for fresh water. On one occasion when we had anchored our little boat under a little point of land, Xury calls to me that we had better go farther off the shore. "For," says he, "there yonder lies a dreadful monster on the side of that hillock, fast asleep."

I looked in the direction where he pointed and saw a huge, wild lion. I shot at the beast from the boat, breaking his leg. He started up on three legs and gave the most hideous roar that I ever heard. I shot again, this time wounding him in the head, whereupon he fell to the ground. Xury, who did not lack courage, jumped into the water, and taking a little gun in one hand, swam to the shore with the other, and coming close to the creature, put the muzzle of the piece to his ear, and with great speed killed the lion at the first shot.

We spent the day getting the hide off him and

spreading it on the top of our cabin. The sun effectually dried it in two days' time, and then I used it to lie upon.

My plan now was to make for the Gambia River or Senegal: that is to say, anywhere about Cape Verde, where I was in hopes of meeting some European ship. For if I did not, I knew not what course I had to take, but to seek the islands or perish among the native people. I knew that all the ships from Europe, which sailed either to the coast of Guinea, or to Brazil, or to the East Indies, made this Cape or those islands.

So, in a word, I risked my life and my fortune upon this single point: either that I must meet with some ship, or must perish.

One afternoon when I was lying down in the cabin, Xury having the helm, the boy suddenly cried out to me, "Master, master, there's a ship with a sail!" I jumped out of the cabin and immediately saw not only the ship, but what she was. It was a Portuguese ship, which I thought must be bound for the Coast of Guinea to capture some slaves.

With all the sail I could make, I found I would not be able to catch up; but after I had crowded to the utmost and began to despair, it seems they saw me with the help of their perspective glasses. So they shortened sail and in about three hours' time I caught up with them.

A Scottish sailor who was on board called to me, and I answered him and told him I was an Englishman, that I had made my escape out of slavery from the Moors at Sallé. They then bade me come on board, and very kindly took me in, with all my goods.

I immediately offered all I had to the captain of the ship as a return for my deliverance, but he generously told me he would take nothing from me, and that all I had would be delivered safe to me when I came to Brazil.

We had a very good voyage to Brazil, and arrived in the Bay de Todos los Santos, or All Saints' Bay, in about twenty-two days.

I will never forget the generous treatment the captain gave me. He would take nothing off me for my passage and gave me forty ducats for the lion's skin. Everything I was willing to sell, he bought off me. In a word, I made about two hundred and twenty pieces of eight for my cargo; and with this stock, I went on shore in Brazil. I should mention that the Captain took my boy Xury, undertaking to set him free in ten years if he agreed to become a Christian.

Seeing how well the planters lived, and how easily they got rich, I resolved, if I could get a permit to settle there, I would turn planter. To this purpose, getting a kind of letter of immigration, I purchased as much uncultivated land as the money I had would allow me to buy.

Near me lived a Portuguese from Lisbon, born of English parents, whose name was Wells. He was in much the same circumstances as I was. His plantation lay next to mine, and we got on very well and sociably together. My stock was low, as was his, and we planted for our own food rather than anything else for about two years. However, we began to have a surplus and our land began to come into order, so that the third year we planted some tobacco, and each made a large piece of ground ready for planting sugar cane the next year.

In the meantime, by the good offices of my kind friend, the captain of the Portuguese ship that took me up at sea, I received the money lying to my credit in London. His ship going there, with the letter of authority with which I had furnished him, he got from the English captain's widow my two hundred pounds. One half of this he invested in English goods and I found means to sell them to a very great advantage, so that I might say I had more than four times the value of my first cargo and was now infinitely better off than Wells in the advancement of my plantation.

Having lived almost four years in Brazil, and beginning to thrive and prosper on my plantation, I had not only learned the language, but had built up acquaintances and friendships among my fellow planters, as well as among the merchants at San Salvador, which was our port.

It happened that, being in company with some merchants and planters of my acquaintance, and talking of the possibilities of trade with the Guinea Coast very earnestly, three of them came to me the next morning to make a proposal to me. After enjoining me to secrecy, they told me that they had a mind to fit out a ship to go to Guinea. The question was whether I would go as their supercargo in the ship, to manage the trading part; and they offered me a share in the profit without the need to provide any part of the stock.

I, who was born to be my own destroyer, could no more resist the offer than I could restrain my first decision to leave home. In a word, I told them I would go if they would undertake to look after my plantation in my absence, and would dispose of it as I directed if it were necessary. This they all agreed to do, and entered into contracts or covenants to do so in case of my death. These made the captain of the ship that saved my life, as before, my universal heir, but obliged him to dispose of my effects as I had directed in my will: that is to say – one half of the produce being for himself, and the other to be shipped to England.

I went on board on the 1st of September, 1659, an evil hour, being the same day eight years before that I left my parents.

We passed the Line after about twelve days and were, by our last observation, in seven degrees twenty-two minutes northern latitude, when a violent wind took us completely off our course. For twelve days together we could do nothing but drive, and, scudding away before the wind, let it carry us wherever fate and its fury would take us.

About the twelfth day, when the weather began to improve, the master made an observation as well as he could. He found that we had come upon the coast of Guiana, or the north part of Brazil, beyond the river Amazon, toward that of the Orinoco, commonly called the Great River. Looking over the charts of the seacoast of South America with him, we concluded that there was no inhabited country for us to have recourse to till we came within the circle of the Caribbean islands, and therefore resolved to head for Barbados. This we might easily do, as we hoped, in about fifteen days' sailing time, whereas we could not possibly make our voyage to the coast of Africa without some repairs, both to our ship and ourselves.

But in the latitude of twelve degrees eighteen minutes, a second storm came upon us. This carried us away with the same impetuosity westward, and drove us so out of the way of all human commerce, that had all our lives been saved from drowning, we stood a greater chance of being devoured by cannibals than ever returning to our own country and seeing our loved ones again.

In this distress, the wind still blowing very hard, one of our men early in the morning cried out, "Land!", and we had no sooner run out of the cabin to look out, in hopes of seeing whereabouts in the world we were, than the ship struck upon sand. In a moment, her motion being so stopped, the sea broke over her in such a manner that we all expected to perish immediately; and we were immediately forced to go into our quarters, to shelter us from the very foam and spray of the sea.

In this disaster, the mate of our vessel laid hold of the lifeboat, and with the help of the rest of the men, flung it over the ship's side. We all got into her, let go, and committed ourselves, being eleven in number, to God's mercy and the wild sea; for though the storm was considerably abated, yet the sea went dreadfully high upon the shore.

After we had rowed, or rather driven, about a league and a half as we reckoned it, a raging wave, mountain-like, came rolling astern of us, and took us with such fury that it overturned the boat at once; and separating us from the boat as well as from one another, it hardly gave us time to say, "O God!", for we were all swallowed up in a moment.

Nothing can describe the confusion of thought which I felt when I sank into the water, for though I swam very well, yet I could not save myself from the waves so as to draw my breath. Finally that wave, having driven me, or rather carried me, a vast way toward the shore, and having spent itself, went back and left me upon the land, almost dry but half dead with the water I took in. I had enough presence of mind, as well as breath left, that seeing myself nearer the main land than I expected, I got up on my feet and attempted to make toward the land as fast as I could before another wave should return and pull me under again; but I soon found it was impossible to avoid it.

Now, as the waves were not as high as the first,

being nearer land, I held onto pieces of rock till the wave abated, and then I ran on a bit farther, which brought me so near the shore that the next wave, though it went over me, did not swamp me so much as to carry me away. The next run I took got me to the main land where, to my great relief, I clambered up the cliffs of the shore, and sat me down upon the grass, free from danger, and right out of the reach of the water.

I was now safe on shore, and began to look up and thank God that my life was saved, when only a few minutes before, there was scarcely any hope of it.

I began to look around me to see what kind of a place I was in, and what was to be done next. I soon found my relief growing less and, in a word, I was in a bad situation. For I was wet, had no clothes but what I wore, and nothing at all to eat or drink or comfort me. The only prospect I saw before me was that of perishing with hunger, or being devoured by wild beasts; and that which was particularly afflicting to me was that I had no weapon either to hunt and kill any creature for my sustenance, or to defend myself against any other creatures that might desire to kill me for theirs.

In a word, I had nothing about me but a knife, a tobacco pipe and a little tobacco. Night coming upon me, I got into a thick bushy tree, and having been excessively fatigued, I fell asleep, and slept as comfortably as, I believe, few could have done in my condition. After this, I was much refreshed and ready to face whatever lay ahead.

CHAPTER THREE

SHIPWRECKED ON THE DESERT ISLAND

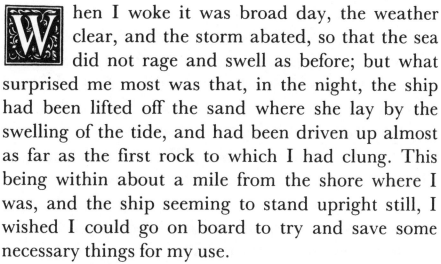hen I woke it was broad day, the weather clear, and the storm abated, so that the sea did not rage and swell as before; but what surprised me most was that, in the night, the ship had been lifted off the sand where she lay by the swelling of the tide, and had been driven up almost as far as the first rock to which I had clung. This being within about a mile from the shore where I was, and the ship seeming to stand upright still, I wished I could go on board to try and save some necessary things for my use.

A little after noon I found the sea very calm, and the tide ebbed so far out that I could come within a quarter of a mile of the ship. I resolved, if possible, to get to it, so I pulled off my clothes, for the weather was extremely hot, and took to the water. But when I came to the ship, my difficulty was to find a way to get on board, for as she lay aground, and high out of the water, there was nothing within my reach to lay hold of.

I swam round her twice, and the second time I spied a small piece of rope, which I wondered how I missed the first time. It hung down by the forechains low enough that with great difficulty I got hold of it, and by the help of that rope got into the forecastle of the ship. Here I found that she lay on the side of a bank of hard sand, or rather earth, so that her stern lay lifted up upon the bank and her head low, almost to the water. By this means, all her quarter was free, and all that was in that part was dry. First, I found that all the ship's provisions were dry and untouched by the water, and being very well disposed to eat, I went to the breadroom and filled my pockets with biscuits, and ate as I went about other things for I had no time to lose. Now I only needed a boat to furnish myself with many things which I foresaw would be very necessary to me.

We had several spare yards, two or three large spars of wood, and a spare topmast or two in the ship. I resolved to build a raft with these, and flung as many overboard as I could manage for their weight, tying every one with a rope so that they would not drift away. When this was done, I went down the ship's side, and pulling them to me, I tied four of them fast together at both ends as well as I could, in the form of a raft. After laying two or three

No inhabited country showed on the charts (page 30)

I clambered up the cliffs of the shore (page 33)

short pieces of plank upon them, diagonally, I found I could walk upon it very well, but that it was not able to bear any great weight, the pieces being too light. So I went to work with a saw I found and cut a spare topmast into three lengths, and added them to my raft, with a great deal of effort and pains. But the hope of furnishing myself with necessities encouraged me to go beyond what I would have been able to do upon another occasion.

My raft was now strong enough to bear any reasonable weight. My next care was what to load it with, and how to preserve what I laid upon it from the surf of the sea; but I was not long considering this. I first laid all the planks or boards that I could get upon it, and having considered well what I most wanted, I got three of the seamen's chests, which I had broken open and emptied, and lowered them down upon my raft; these I filled with provisions. Then I looked for tools to work with on shore, and it was after long searching that I found the carpenter's chest, which was indeed a very useful prize to me, and much more valuable than a ship full of gold would have been at that time. I got it down to my raft, whole and safe, without taking the time to look into it, for I knew in general what it contained.

My next concern was for some ammunition and

arms. There were two very good fowling pieces in the great cabin and two pistols. These I took, along with some powder horns and a small bag of shot, and two old rusty swords. I knew there were three barrels of powder in the ship, and with much search I found them. Two of them were dry and good, the third ruined by the water. Those two I got on my raft with the arms. And now I thought myself pretty well stocked, and began to think how I could get on shore with them, having neither sail, oar, nor rudder, and easy prey to the least capful of wind. I hoped to find some creek or river which I might make use of as a port to get to land with my cargo.

As I imagined, so it was! There appeared before me a little opening of the land, and I found a strong current of the tide set into it. So I guided my raft, as well as I could, to get into the middle of the stream.

At length I spied a little cove on the right shore of the creek to which, with great pain and difficulty, I guided my raft. At last I got so near that, reaching ground with my oar, I could thrust her directly in; and there I lay till the water ebbed away, and left my raft and all my cargo safe on shore.

My next job was to survey the country and seek a proper place for my habitation, and where to store my goods to keep them safe from whatever might happen to me during my time there.

There was a hill not more than a mile from me, which rose up very steep and high, and which seemed to be higher than some other hills that lay as in a ridge from it, northward. From the top of this hill I saw my fate, to my great distress. I was on an island, surrounded on every side by the sea, no land to be seen except some rocks which lay a great way off, and two small islands, smaller than mine, which lay about three leagues to the west.

I now began to think that I should get a great many more things out of the ship which would be useful and necessary to me, and particularly some of the rigging and sails, and I resolved to make another trip out and board the vessel, if possible. And as I knew that the first storm that came up would certainly break her all in pieces, I resolved to let everything else wait till I got everything that I could get out of the ship.

I got on board the ship as before and prepared a second raft; and having had experience of the first, I made this one less unwieldy, and loaded it less fully. Still I brought away several things very useful to me. First, in the carpenter's stores, I found two of three bags of nails and spikes, a great screw jack, a dozen or two hatchets, and, above all, that most useful thing called a grindstone. All these I secured together, with several things belonging to the gunner, particularly, two or three iron crowbars, and two barrels of musket bullets, seven muskets, and another fowling piece, with another small quantity of powder, and a large bag full of small shot. I found a great roll of sheet lead, but this last was so heavy that I could not hoist it up to get it over the ship's side. Beside these things, I took all the men's clothes that I could find, and a spare fore topsail, a hammock, and some bedding; and with these I loaded my second rough raft, and brought them all safe on shore, to my very great relief.

Having got my second cargo on shore, though I had to open the barrels of powder and bring their contents in small amounts, for they were too heavy, being large casks, I went to work to make a little tent with the sails and some poles which I cut for that purpose. And into this tent I brought everything that I knew would spoil either with rain or sun, and I piled all the empty chests and casks up in a circle round the tent to fortify it from any sudden attack from either man or beast.

I now had the biggest stockpile of all kinds that ever was laid up, I believe, for one man, but I was not yet satisfied; for while the ship sat in that upright posture, I thought I ought to get everything out of her that I could. So, every day at low water, I went on board and brought away something or other. One visit I discovered a locker containing about thirty-six pounds value in money, some European coin, some pieces of eight, some gold, some silver.

I had now been thirteen days ashore, and had been eleven times on board the ship. In that time I had brought away all that one pair of hands could well be supposed capable of bringing, though I truly believe, had the calm weather held, I would have brought away the whole ship, piece by piece; but preparing to go on board the twelfth time, I found the wind was beginning to rise, and before it was high tide, a storm blew up.

But I was home in my little tent, where I lay in snug safety with all my wealth around me. It blew very hard all that night, and in the morning when I looked out, behold the ship was no more to be seen! I was a little surprised, but recovered myself with the satisfactory reflection that I had lost no time, nor spared any effort, to get everything out of her that could be useful to me, and that, indeed, there was little left in her that I was able to bring away, even if I had found more time.

My thoughts were now wholly employed in making

myself safe either against enemies, if any should appear, or wild beasts, if any were in the island. I decided I would make myself both a cave and a tent, the manner and description of which it may not be improper to give an account of.

I soon decided the place I was in was not good for settlement, particularly because it was upon low marsh ground near the sea, and I believed it would not be healthy, and more particularly, because there was no fresh water near it. So I resolved to find a healthier and more convenient spot of ground.

In searching for this, I found a little plain on the side of a rising hill, whose front toward this plain was as steep as a houseside, so that nothing could come down upon me from the top. On the side of this rock, there was a hollow place, worn a little way in like the entrance or door of a cave, but there was not really a cave or way into the rock at all.

On the flat of the green, just before this hollow place, I resolved to pitch my tent. This plain was not more than one hundred yards broad and about twice as long, and lay like a meadow before my door. At the end, it descended irregularly every way down into the low ground by the seaside. It was on the north-northwest side of the hill so that it was sheltered from the heat every day, till it came to a west and by south sun or thereabouts, which, in those countries, is near the setting.

Before I set up my tent, I drew a half-circle in front of the hollow place, which took in about ten yards in its half diameter from the rock, and twenty yards in its diameter from its beginning to its ending.

On this half circle I pitched two rows of strong stakes, driving them into the ground till they stood very firm like piles, the biggest end being out of the ground about five feet and a half, and sharpened on the top. The two rows stood not more than six inches from one another.

I made the entrance into this place not a door, but a short ladder going over the top. When I was in, I lifted this ladder over after me and so I was completely fenced in and fortified from all the world. By this means I felt safe and slept secure in the night, which otherwise I could not have done. As it happened afterward, there was no need for all this caution against the enemies I thought I might be in danger from.

Into this fence, or fortress, with infinite work I carried all my riches. Then I made a large tent, which, to preserve me from the rains, I made double. That is, one smaller tent within, and one larger tent above it, and covered the uppermost one with a large tarpaulin which I had saved along with the sails.

And now I no longer took my rest in the bed which I had brought on shore, but in a hammock, which had belonged to the mate of the ship and was a very good one.

Into this tent I brought all my provisions, and everything that would spoil in the wet; and having thus enclosed all my goods, I filled in the entrance, which till now I had left open, and so went in and out, as I have said, by a short ladder.

When I had done this, I began to work my way into the rock; then, bringing all the earth and stones that I dug out through my tent, I laid them within my fence in the nature of a terrace, so that it raised the ground within about a foot and a half. In this way I made me a cave just behind my tent, which served me like a cellar to my house. It took a lot of work and many days before all these things were brought to perfection, and therefore, I must go back to tell of some other things which happened meanwhile.

While I was building and working on my living quarters, I went out at least once every day with my gun. One day I killed a goat, which had a little kid by her. This grieved me heartily. When the mother goat fell, the kid stood stock still by her till I came and picked her up; and not only so, but when I carried the old one with me upon my shoulders, the kid followed me right to my enclosure. Upon this, I laid down the nanny and took the kid in my arms, and carried it over my fence, in hopes to make it tame and useful. But it would not eat, so I was forced to kill it and eat it myself. These two supplied me with flesh a long while, for I ate sparingly and preserved my provisions (my bread especially) as much as I possibly could.

It was, by my account, the 30th of September when I first set foot upon this horrid island.

After I had been there about ten or twelve days, it came into my thoughts that I would lose all track of time, and might even forget the Sabbath day from working days, if I did not set my mind to it. So, to prevent this, I made a large cross from some posts and set it up on the shore where I first landed. With my knife, I cut this message into the wood: I CAME ON SHORE HERE ON THE 30th SEPTEMBER, 1659. Upon the sides of this square post I cut a notch with my knife every day, and every seventh notch was twice as long as the rest, and every first day of the month as long again as that long one. Thus I made my calendar, and kept a weekly, monthly, and yearly account of time.

I must tell you now that, among the many things

which I brought out of the ship, there are several things that I omitted to mention. These included three very good Bibles and several other books, all of which I carefully made safe. And I must not forget that we had a dog and two cats on the ship. I carried both the cats with me. As for the dog, he jumped out of the ship himself, and swam on shore the day after I went on shore with my first cargo, and was a trusty servant to me for many years. I wanted for nothing that was in his power to fetch me, nor any company that he could provide for me. My only wish was to have him talk to me, but that he could not do.

The lack of tools made hard work of every job I did, and it was nearly a whole year before I had finished my little fence, or surrounded my habitation. But I didn't need to be concerned at the tediousness of anything I had to do, for I had time enough to do it in as I had no other employment. Once I finished my fortress, I could foresee nothing to do except to explore the island and look for food, which I did more or less every day anyway.

I have already described my habitation, which was a tent under the side of a rock, surrounded with a strong fence of posts and cables. But I might now call it a wall, for I raised a kind of wall against it of turfs, about two feet thick on the outside. After some time

(I think it was a year and a half), I raised rafters from it leaning to the rock, and thatched or covered it with boughs of trees and such things. This was to keep out the rain, which I found very violent at some times of the year.

I have already told how I brought all my goods inside the fence and into the cave which I had made behind me. But I must also say that, at first, this was a confused heap of goods, which, as they lay in no order, so they took up all my place.

I had no room to turn around in, so I set myself to enlarge my cave and work farther into the earth, for it was a loose, sandy rock which yielded easily to the work I bestowed upon it; and when I found I was pretty safe from the beasts of prey, I worked sideways, to the right hand, into the rock, and then, turning to the right again, worked out, and made myself a door that would lead to the outside of my fortification.

This not only gave me a back way to my tent and to my storehouse as it were, but also gave me room to arrange my goods.

And it was now that I began to keep a journal of every day's employment and happenings; for, indeed, at first, I not only had much too much work to do, but also was in much discomposure of mind, and my journal would have been full of many dull things. But having solved some of the everyday problems; having settled my household stuff and habitation; and having made me a table and a chair, and all about me as handsome as I could, I began to keep my journal. I shall here give you some extracts from it for as long as it lasted, for, having no more ink, I was forced to give it up.

CHAPTER FOUR
CRUSOE'S JOURNAL

ov. 4: This morning I began to record my times of work, of going out with my gun, of sleep, and of diversion. Every morning I walked out with my gun for two or three hours if it did not rain, and then employed myself in work till about eleven o'clock. Then I ate what I had to live on, and from twelve to two I lay down to sleep, the weather being excessively hot. And then, in the evening, I went to work again. The working part of this day and the next was wholly employed in making my table, for I was as yet but a very poor carpenter.

Later, time and necessity made of me a good, natural man of all trades, as I believe they would anyone else under similar conditions.

Nov. 17: This day I began to dig behind my tent, into the rock, to make a room much like a cellar which would stay cool.

Note: Three things I needed very badly for this work were a pickaxe, a shovel and a wheelbarrow or basket. So I desisted from my work and began to consider how to supply these wants, and make me some tools. For the pickaxe, I made use of the iron crows, which were proper enough, though heavy. The next thing was a shovel or spade, and this was so absolutely necessary that, indeed, I could do nothing effectually without it. But what kind of one to make I knew not.

Nov. 18: The next day, in searching the woods, I found a tree of that wood, or like it, which in Brazil they call the iron tree because of its exceeding hardness. From this, with great effort, and almost spoiling my axe, I cut a piece and brought it home, with difficulty enough, for it was exceedingly heavy. The excessive hardness of the wood, and my having such poor tools, made a very long and hard job of it, for I worked it effectually little by little into the form of a shovel or spade. The handle was shaped exactly like ours in England, only that the board part, having no iron shod upon it at the bottom, would not last me so long. However, it served well enough for the uses which I had occasion to put it to, but never was a shovel, I believe, made in that fashion or so long in making.

Nov. 23: My other work having now stood still, because of my making these tools, when they were finished I went on. I worked solidly every day, as my strength and time allowed, until I had spent eighteen days entirely in widening and deepening my cave, that it might hold my goods without great crowding.

Dec. 17: From this day to the 20th, I placed shelves, and knocked up nails on the posts to hang everything up that could be hung up; and now I began to feel I had made some doors.

Dec. 20: I carried everything into the cave, and began to furnish my house and set up some pieces of boards, like a dresser, to arrange my victuals upon, but boards began to be very scarce with me; also I made me another table.

Dec. 28, 29, 30, 31: Great heat and no breeze. I was not able to stir outside, except in the evening, for food. This time I spent in putting all my things in order within doors.

Jan. 1: Very hot still, but I went outside early and late with my gun, and lay still in the middle of the day. This evening, going farther into the valleys which lay toward the middle of the islands, I found there were plenty of goats, though exceedingly shy and hard to get near to. However, I thought that, if I could not get close, I would bring my dog to hunt them down. Accordingly, the next day, I went with my dog and set him upon the goats. But I was mistaken, for they all turned on the dog, and he knew his danger too well, for he would not come near them.

Jan. 3: I began my fence or wall, which, since I was still fearful of being attacked by somebody, I resolved to make very thick and strong.

In the middle of all my work, it happened that in rummaging in my things, I found a little bag which had been filled with corn for the feeding of poultry. What little remainder of corn had been in the bag was all devoured by the rats, and I saw nothing in the bag but husks and dust; and wanting to have the bag for some other possible use, I shook the husks of corn out of it on one side of my fortification, under the rock.

It was a short time before the great rain I mentioned that I threw this stuff away. About a month after, I saw some few stalks of something green shooting out of the ground. I was perfectly astonished when, after a longer time, I saw about ten or twelve ears come out, which were perfect green barley of the same kind as our European, nay, of our English barley.

I carefully saved the ears of this corn, you may be sure, in their season, which was about the end of June; and laying up every corn, I resolved to sow

I loaded my second raft and brought it safe on shore
(page 42)

I carried the kid in my arms over my fence (page 47)

them all again, hoping, in time, to have a quantity sufficient to supply me with bread. But it was not till the fourth year that I could allow myself the least grain of this corn to eat, and even then but sparingly, as I shall show afterward in its order. For I lost all that I sowed the first season by not observing the proper time. For I made the mistake of sowing just before the dry season so that it never came up at all, at least not as it should have done: of which in its place.

Beside this barley, there were, as above, twenty to thirty stalks of rice, which I preserved with the same care, and whose use was to be of the same kind or to the same purpose, to make me bread, or rather food. For I found ways to cook it up without baking, though I did that also after some time. But to return to my journal.

I worked excessively hard these three or four months to get my wall done, and on the 14th of April I closed it up.

April 16: I finished the ladder, so I went up with the ladder to the top, and then pulled it up after me and let it down on the inside. This was a complete enclosure to me, for within it I had plenty of room, and nothing could come at me from outside unless it could first mount my wall.

The very next day after this wall was finished, I almost had all my work ruined at once, and myself killed. The case was thus. As I was busy in the inside of it, behind my tent just at the entrance into my cave, I was terribly frightened by earth tumbling down from the roof of my cave. Fearing that I might be buried alive I ran to my ladder and climbed over my wall, when I found that there was an appalling earthquake.

I was so much amazed with the thing itself that I was like one stupefied, and the motion of the earth made my stomach sick, like one that was tossed at sea. But the noise of the falling of the rock woke me, as it were, rousing me from the stupefied condition I was in. It filled me with horror, and I thought of nothing but the hill falling upon my tent and my household goods and burying all at once; this sank my very soul within me a second time and I felt greatly discouraged.

After the third shock was over, and I felt no more for some time, I began to take courage.

June 16: Going down to the seaside, I found a large tortoise, or turtle. This was the first I had seen, which, it seems, was only to my misfortune, not any defect of the place or scarcity; for had I happened to be on the other side of the island, I might have had hundreds of them every day as I found afterward; but perhaps at a dear price.

June 17: I spent time in cooking the turtle. I found in her three score eggs, and her flesh was to me, at that time, the most delicious and pleasant that I ever tasted in my life, having had no flesh but of goats and fowls since I landed in this horrid place.

June 18: Rained all day, and I stayed inside. I thought at this time the rain felt cold, and I was somewhat chilly, which I knew was not usual in that latitude.

June 19: Very ill, and shivering as if the weather had been cold.

June 20: No rest all night; violent pains in my head, and feverish.

June 21: Very ill; frightened almost to death with the apprehensions of my sad condition: to be sick, and no help. Prayed to God for the first time since the storm off Hull, but scarce knew what I said, or why, my thoughts were so confused.

June 22: A little better, but under dreadful apprehensions of sickness.

June 23: Very bad again; cold and shivering, and then a violent headache.

June 24: Much better.

June 25: An ague very violent. The fit held me

seven hours; cold fit, and hot, with faint sweats after it.

June 26: Better, and having no victuals to eat, took my gun, but found myself very weak. However, I killed a goat, and with much difficulty got it home, and broiled some of it, and ate. I would have stewed it, and made some broth, but had no pot.

June 27: The ague again so violently that I lay abed, all day, and neither ate nor drank. I was ready to perish for thirst, but so weak I had not the strength to stand up or get myself any water to drink. Prayed to God again, but was light-headed; and when I was not, I was so ignorant that I knew not what to say, only lay and cried, "Lord, look upon me! Lord, pity me! Lord, have mercy upon me!" I suppose I did nothing else for two or three hours, till the fit wearing off, I fell asleep and did not wake till far in the night.

When I awoke I found myself much refreshed, but weak, and exceedingly thirsty. However, as I had no water in my whole habitation, I was forced to lie till morning.

The 30th was my well day, and I went abroad with my gun, but did not dare to travel too far. I killed a seafowl or two, something like a brent goose, and brought them home, but was not very keen to eat them. So I ate some more of the turtle's eggs, which were very good and not difficult to digest.

I was not so well the next day, which was the 1st of July, as I hoped I should have been; for I had a small attack of the cold fit, but it was not severe and I felt my strength had returned.

July 4: In the morning I took the Bible, and beginning at the New Testament, I began seriously to read it. I set myself a resolution to read awhile every morning and every night, not binding myself to the number of chapters, but going on as long as my thoughts should engage me.

It was on the 15th of July that I began to take a more particular survey of the island itself. I went up the creek first, where, as I hinted, I brought my raft on shore. I found, after I came about two miles up, that the tide did not flow any higher, and that it was no more than a little brook of running water, very fresh and good. But this being the dry season, there was hardly any water in some parts of it, at least, not a real stream.

On the banks of this brook I found many pleasant grasslands or meadows, plain, smooth, and covered with grass; and on the rising parts of them, next to the higher grounds (where the water, as it might be supposed, never overflowed), I found a great deal of tobacco, green, and growing to a very great and strong stalk; and there were many other plants, which I had no knowledge of.

The next day, the 16th, I went up the same way again, and after going something farther than I had gone the day before, I found the brook and the grasslands begin to cease, and the country become more woody than before. In this part I found different fruit, and particularly, I found melons upon the ground in great abundance and grapes upon the trees. The vines, indeed, had spread over the trees, and the clusters of grapes were now just in their prime, very ripe and rich.

This was a surprising discovery, and I was exceedingly glad of them. I found an excellent use for these grapes, and that was to cure or dry them in the sun, and keep them as dried grapes or raisins are kept, which I thought would be as wholesome and as agreeable to eat when no grapes were to be had. As I found that I could not carry the grapes without spoiling them, I gathered a large number and hung them in clusters upon the out branches of adjacent trees. As raisins they could be transported easily and without damage.

Having spent three days in this journey, I came back home, as I must now call my enclosed tent and my cave.

When I returned from this journey, I began to consider removing my habitation to this fruitful part of the island.

I was so taken with this place that I spent much of my time there for the whole remaining part of the month of July; and though, upon second thoughts, I resolved not to move there, I built me a little kind of a bower, and surrounded it at a distance with a strong fence, being a double hedge as high as I could reach, well-staked, and filled between the brushwood.

Here I lay very secure sometimes two or three nights together, always going over it with a ladder, as before: so that I now fancied I had my country and my seacoast house. This work took me up to the beginning of August.

Sept. 30: I was now come to the unhappy anniversary of my landing. I counted up the notches on my post and found I had been on shore three hundred and sixty-five days. I kept this day as a solemn fast, setting it apart for religious exercise. A little after this, my ink beginning to run out, I contented myself to use it more sparingly, and to write down only the most remarkable events of my life.

While my corn was growing, I made a little

discovery, which was of use to me afterward. As soon as the rains were over, and the weather began to settle, which was about the month of November, I made a visit up the country to my bower. Here, though I had not been for some months, I found all things just as I had left them. The circle or double hedge that I had made was not only firm and whole, but the stakes which I had cut out of trees that grew thereabouts were all shot out and grown with long branches.

I was very well pleased to see the young trees grow, and I pruned them, and led them to grow as much alike as I could, and it is scarce credible how beautiful a shape they grew into in three years so that, though the hedge made a circle of about twenty-five yards in diameter, yet the trees soon covered it, and it was a complete shade, sufficient to live under all the dry season. This made me resolve to cut some more stakes and make me a hedge like this in a semicircle round my wall (I mean that of my first dwelling), which I did: and placing the trees or stakes in a double row, at about eight yards distance from my fence, they soon grew and were at first a fine cover to my habitation, and afterward served for a defence also, as I shall tell in its order.

CHAPTER FIVE
JACK OF ALL TRADES

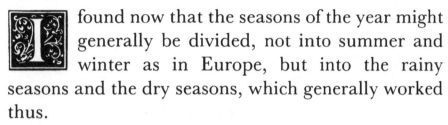

found now that the seasons of the year might generally be divided, not into summer and winter as in Europe, but into the rainy seasons and the dry seasons, which generally worked thus.

From the middle of February to the middle of April, rainy, the sun being then on or near the equinox. From the middle of April till the middle of August, dry, the sun being then north of the Line. From the middle of August till the middle of October, rainy, the sun then having come back to the Line. From the middle of October till the middle of February, dry, the sun being then to the south of the Line.

After I had found, by experience, the ill consequences of being out in the rain, I took care to furnish myself with provisions beforehand, that I might not be obliged to go out, and I sat within doors as much as possible during the wet months.

During this wet time, I found much employment

making baskets, using twigs of that tree from which I cut my stakes. In one of my journeys, my dog surprised a young kid and seized it, and I, running to take hold it, caught it and saved it from the dog. I had a great mind to bring it home if I could, for I had often been musing whether it might not be possible to get a kid or two, and so raise a breed of tame goats, which might supply me with food when my powder and shot were all spent. I made a collar for this little creature, and with a string which I made of some rope yarn, which I always carried about me, I led him along, though with some difficulty, till I came to my bower, and there I enclosed him lest he try to escape.

In time the creature became so loving, so gentle, and so fond of me, that it was from that time one of my household also, and would never leave me afterward.

In the months of November and December, I expected my crop of barley and rice. The ground I had manured or dug up for them was not large, for, as I observed, my seed of each was not more than half a peck, having lost one whole crop by sowing in the dry season. But now my crop promised very well, when, suddenly, I found I was in danger of losing it again by enemies of several sorts, which it was scarce possible to keep from it. First there were the goats, and wild creatures which I called hares, who, tasting the sweetness of the blade, lay in it night and day, as soon as it came up, and ate it so close to the ground that it had no time to shoot up into stalk.

I saw no remedy for this except to make an enclosure about it with a hedge, which I did with a great deal of toil, all the more because it required speed.

However, as my arable land was small, suited to my crop, I got it tolerably well fenced in about three weeks' time; and shooting some of the creatures in the daytime, I set my dog to guard it at night, tying him up to a stake at the gate where he would stand and bark all night long. So in a little while the enemies forsook the place and the corn grew very strong and well, and began to ripen.

But as the beasts ruined me before, while my corn was in the blade, so the birds were likely to ruin me now, when it was in the ear. For going along by the place to see how it was thriving, I saw my little crop surrounded with fowls, I knew not of how many sorts, who stood, as it were, watching till I should be gone. I immediately let fly among them, for I always had my gun with me, and killed three of them. I took them up and treated them as we treat notorious thieves in England: hanged them in chains, for a lesson to others.

It is impossible to imagine that this would have the effect it did, for the fowls not only never came to the corn, but, in short, they forsook all that part of the island, and I could never see a bird near the place as long as my scarecrows hung there. This I was very glad of, you may be sure; and about the latter end of December, which was our second harvest of the year, I reaped my corn.

When it rained and I could not go out, I found employment making myself some earthen vessels, which indeed I very much needed, but knew not where to come by them. However, considering the heat of the climate, I did not doubt that if I could but find some clay, I might botch up some such pot which might, being dried in the sun, be hard and strong enough to bear handling, and to hold anything that was dry, and required to be kept so; and as this was necessary in preparing corn, meal, and such, which was the thing I was upon, I resolved to make some as large as I could, and well fit to stand like jars, to hold what should be put into them until it was needed.

It would make the reader pity me, or rather laugh at me, to tell how many awkward ways I took to raise this paste; what odd, misshapen, ugly things I made; how many of them fell in, and how many fell out, the clay not being stiff enough to bear its own weight; and, in a word, how, after having worked hard to find the clay, to dig it, to temper it, to bring it home, and work it, I could not make more than two large, earthen ugly things (I cannot call them jars) in about two months.

But all this would not answer my end: which was to get an earthen pot to hold liquids and bear the fire, which none of these could. I happened some time after, making a pretty large fire for cooking my meat, when I went to put it out after I had done with it, that I found a broken piece of one of my earthenware vessels in the fire, burned as hard as a stone and red as a tile. I was agreeably surprised to see it, and said to myself that certainly they might be made to burn whole, if they would burn broken.

This set me to study how to arrange my fire so as to make it burn some pots.

I had no notion of a kiln, such as the potters burn in, or of glazing them with lead, though I had some lead to do it with; but I placed three pipkins and two or three pots in a pile, one upon another, and placed my firewood all round it, with a great heap of embers under them. I plied the fire with fresh fuel round the outside and upon the top, till I saw pots in the inside red-hot quite through, and observed that they did not crack at all.

When I saw them clear red, I let them stand in that heat about five or six hours, till I found one of them, though it did not crack, melt or run, for all the sand which was mixed with the clay melted by the violence of the heat, and would have run into glass if I had gone on. So I slacked my fire gradually, till the pots began to abate of the redness; and watching them all night, that I might not let the fire abate too fast, in the morning I had three very good, I will not say handsome, pipkins, and two other earthen pots, as hard as could be desired; and one of them perfectly glazed with the running of the sand. After this I made every kind of earthenware I needed, but I cannot praise the shapes of them for they left much to be desired in their design.

In the third year, my stock of corn increasing, I really wanted to build my barns bigger. I wanted a place to lay it up in, for the increase of the corn now yielded me so much that I had of the barley about twenty bushels, and of rice as much or more. So now I resolved to begin to use it freely, for my bread had been quite gone a long while. I resolved also to see what quantity would be sufficient to last me a whole year, and to sow but once a year and so save my energy for other work.

Upon the whole, I found that the forty bushels of barley and rice were much more than I could consume in a year, so I resolved to sow just the same quantity every year that I sowed the last, in hopes that such a quantity would fully provide me with bread and such.

All this time, you may be sure, my thoughts ran many times upon the prospect of land which I had seen from the other side of the island, and I was not without some secret wish that I was on shore there. I had the idea that, seeing the mainland and an inhabited country, I might find some way or other to convey myself farther, and perhaps at last find some means of escape. Then I thought I would go and look at our ship's boat, which had been blown up quite far upon the shore in the storm, when we were first cast away.

She lay nearly where she did at first, but not quite, having turned by the force of the waves and the winds almost bottom upward, against a high ridge of beachy rough sand; but there was no water about her. If I had had other pairs of hands to refit her, and to have launched her into the water, the boat would have done very well, and I might have gone back into

Brazil with her easily enough; but I might have foreseen that alone I could no more turn her and set her upright upon her bottom than I could remove the island.

At length I began to think whether it was possible to make myself a canoe, or periagua, such as the natives of those climates make, even without tools, or, as I might say, without help of the trunk of a great tree.

I felled a cedar tree, and I questioned much whether Solomon ever had such a one for the building of the Temple at Jerusalem. It was five feet ten inches in diameter at the lower part next to the stump, and four feet eleven inches in diameter at the end of twenty-two feet, where it lessened and then parted into branches.

It was with hard work that I felled this tree. I was twenty days hacking at the bottom, and fourteen more getting the branches and limbs and the vast spreading head of it cut off. After this, it took me a month to shape it and dub it to a proportion, and to something like the bottom of a boat, that it might swim upright as it ought to do. It took me near three months more to clear the inside, and work it out so as to make an exact boat of it. This I did, indeed, without fire, by mere mallet and chisel, and by the

The goats all turned on the dog (page 54)

The noise of the falling rock woke me (page 58)

dint of hard effort, till I had made of it a very handsome canoe that was big enough to have carried me and all my cargo.

But all my attempts to get it into the water failed me, though they took an inexpressible effort too, for I could no more move the canoe than I could the other boat.

This grieved me heartily. And now I saw, though too late, the folly of beginning a job before carefully counting the cost in time and effort, and before judging rightly of our own strength and determination to go through with it.

In the middle of this work, I finished my fourth year in this place, and kept my anniversary with the same devotion and with as much comfort as I had done in years before.

I now began to consider how to put the few rags I had, which I called clothes, into some order. I had saved the skins of all the creatures that I killed, I mean four-footed ones, and I had hung them up, stretched out with sticks, in the sun, by which means some of them were so dry and hard that they were not fit for much, but others I found very useful.

The first thing I made of these was a cap for my head, with the hair on the outside, to shoot off the rain; and this I performed so well, that I made me a suit of clothes wholly of the skins, that is to say, a waistcoat, and breeches open at the knees, and both loose, for they were more to keep me cool than warm.

After this, I spent a great deal of time and pains to make me an umbrella. I made one and covered it with skins, the hair upwards, so that it cast off the rain like a pent-house, and kept off the sun so effectively that I could walk out in the hottest of weather with greater advantage than I could before in the coolest; and when I had no need of it, could close it and carry it under my arm with the least amount of inconvenience.

Thus I lived mighty comfortably, my mind being entirely composed by resigning to the will of God, and throwing myself wholly upon the disposal of His providence.

I cannot say that for five years after this any extraordinary thing happened to me, but I lived on in the same course, in the same way and place just as before. The chief things I was employed in, besides my yearly task of planting my barley and rice and curing my raisins, both of which I always kept up just enough to have sufficient stock of one year's provision beforehand. I say, besides this yearly work, and my daily pursuit of going out with my gun, I had one task, to make me a canoe, which at last I finished.

Then, by digging a canal for it, six feet wide and four feet deep, I brought it into the creek, almost half a mile.

However, though my little canoe was finished, the size of it was not at all answerable to the plan which I had in view when I started to make it: I mean, of venturing over to the *terra firma*, where it was more than forty miles broad. Accordingly, the smallness of my boat helped to put an end to that plan, and now I thought no more of it.

In happy control of my feelings, I remained near a year and lived a very sedate, retired life, as you may well suppose; and my thoughts being very much composed as to my condition, and fully comforted in resigning myself to the dispositions of Providence, I thought I lived very happily in all things, except that of missing most severely the company and companionship of human society.

I improved myself in this time in all the mechanic exercises which my necessities made me apply myself to, and I believe I could, upon occasion, have made a very good carpenter, especially considering how few tools I had.

Beside this, I arrived at an unexpected perfection in my earthenware, and contrived well enough to make them a wheel, which I found infinitely easier and better. Now I made things round and with shape, which before were filthy things indeed to look upon.

CHAPTER SIX

THE FOOTPRINT ON THE SANDS

eing now in the eleventh year of my residence, and my ammunition growing low, I set myself to study some art to trap and snare the goats, to see whether I could not catch some of them alive.

I started by digging myself several large pits in the earth, in places where I had observed the goats used to feed, and over those pits I placed hurdles of my own making, with a great weight upon them. I set three traps in one night, and the next morning, I found three kids, a male and two females in one. Taking them one by one, I tied them together with strings, and with some difficulty brought them all home.

It was a good while before they would feed, but when I threw them some sweet corn, it tempted them, and they began to be tame. Now I found that if I expected to supply myself with goats' flesh when I had no powder or shot left, breeding some to be tame was my only way, and I might have them about my house like a flock of sheep. But then it occurred to me that I must keep the tame from the wild, or else they would always run wild when they grew up.

The only way for this was to have some enclosed ground, well fenced either with hedge or posts, to keep them in so effectually that those inside might not break out, or those outside break in. For a start, I made an enclosure one hundred and fifty yards by one hundred, to which, as my flocks increased, I added. In about a year and a half, I had a flock of about twelve goats, kids and all, and in two years more I had forty-three, beside several that I had killed for food.

But this was not all, for now I set up my dairy, and had sometimes a gallon or two of milk in a day. And as Nature, who gives supplies of food to every creature, dictates naturally how to make use of it, so I, after a great many tries and miscarriages, made me both butter and cheese at last, and also salt (though I found it partly made to my hand by the heat of the sun upon some of the rocks of the sea), and never was in want of it afterward. All of this made me well pleased with myself.

It would have made a stoic smile to have seen me and my little family sit down to dinner. There was I, the prince and lord of the whole island. I had the lives of all my subjects at my absolute command. I could hang, draw, give liberty, and take it away; and no rebels among all my subjects.

Then, to see how like a king I dined too, all alone, attended by my servants! Poll, as if he had been my pet, was the only person permitted to talk to me. My dog, who was now grown very old and crazy, and two cats, one on one side of the table, and one on the other, expecting now and then a bit from my hand, as a mark of special regard.

You are to understand that now I had, as I may call it, two plantations in the island: one my little fortification or tent with the wall about it, under the rock, with the cave behind me, which, by this time, I had enlarged into several apartments or caves, one within another.

One of these, which was the driest and largest and had a door out beyond my wall or fortification (that is to say, beyond where my wall joined to the rock), was all filled up with the large earthen pots of which I have given an account, and with fourteen or fifteen great baskets, which would hold five or six bushels each. There I laid up my stores of provision, especially my corn, some in the ear, cut off short from the straw, and the other rubbed out with my hand.

As for my wall, made, as before, with long stakes

or piles, all those piles grew like trees and were by this time grown so big, and spread so very much, that there was not the least appearance, to anyone's view, of any habitation behind them.

Near this dwelling of mine, but a little farther within the land and upon lower ground, lay my two pieces of corn land, which I kept and duly cultivated and sowed. They in their turn duly yielded me their harvest in its season; and whenever I had occasion for more corn, I had more good land adjoining that.

Beside this, I had my country seat, and I now had a tolerable plantation there also. First, I had my little bower, as I called it, which I kept in repair (that is to say, I kept the hedge which encircled it trimmed constantly to its usual height, the ladder standing always on the inside). I kept the trees, which at first were no more than my stakes, but were now grown very firm and tall, always cut, so that they might spread and grow thick and wild, and make the more agreeable shade, which they did most effectually, to my mind. In the middle of this, I had my tent always standing, being a piece of sail spread over poles, set up for that purpose, and which never lacked any repair or renewing. And under this I had made me a squab or couch with the skins of the creatures I had killed, and with other soft things; and a blanket laid on them, such as belonged to our sea beddings which I had saved from the wreck, and a great overcoat to cover me. And here, whenever I had occasion to be absent from my chief seat, I took up my country habitation.

It happened one day, about noon, going toward my boat, I was exceedingly surprised by the print of a man's bare foot on the shore, which was very plain to be seen in the sand. I stood like one thunderstruck, or as if I had seen an apparition. I listened. I looked around me, but I could hear nothing, nor could I see anything. I went up to some rising ground to look farther. I went up the shore and down the shore, but it was the same everywhere. I could see no other impression but that one. I went to it again to see if there were any more, and to observe if it might not be my imagination. But it was not, for there was exactly the print of a foot: toes, heel, and every part of a foot.

How it came thither I knew not, nor could I in the least imagine; but, after innumerable fluttering thoughts, like a man completely confused and out of sorts with myself, I came home to my fortification, not feeling, as we say, the ground I went on, but terrified to the last degree, looking behind me at every two or three steps, mistaking every bush and tree, and fancying every stump at a distance to be the threatening shadow of a man.

When I came to my castle, I fled into it like one pursued; whether I went over by the ladder, as first contrived, or went in at the hole in the rock, which I had called a door, I cannot remember. No, nor could I remember the next morning, for never a frightened hare fled to cover, or a fox to earth with more terror of mind than I to this retreat.

Now I began to take courage and to peep outside again, for I had not stirred out of my castle for three days and nights, so that I began to starve for provisions; for I had little or nothing within doors but some barley cakes and water. Then, I knew too, that my goats wanted to be milked.

Encouraging myself, therefore, with the belief that this was nothing but the print of one of my own feet, I began to be a little bolder, and to think there was really nothing in it but my own imagination. But I could not persuade myself fully of this unless I went down to the shore again. When I arrived at the place and came to measure the mark with my own foot, I found my foot not as large by a great deal. This filled my head with new imaginations so that I shook with cold like one in an ague. I went home again, filled with the belief that some man or men had been on shore there, or in short, that the island was inhabited, and I might be surprised before I was aware; and what course to take for my security, I knew not.

Now I began sorely to repent that I had dug my cave so large as to bring a door through again, which door, as I said, came out beyond where my fortification joined to the rock. Upon maturely considering this, therefore, I resolved to build a second fortification, in the same manner of a semicircle, at a distance from my wall, just where I had planted a double row of trees about twelve years before, of which I made mention.

These trees had been planted so thickly before, they needed but a few piles to be driven between them, that they might be thicker and stronger, and my wall would soon be finished, so that I now had a double wall; and my outer was thickened with pieces of timber, old cables, and everything I could think of to make it strong, having in it seven little holes, about as big as I might put my arm through.

On the inside of this, I thickened my wall to about ten feet by continually bringing earth out of my cave, laying it at the foot of the wall, and walking upon it; and through the seven holes I contrived to plant the muskets, of which I took notice that I had brought seven on shore out of the ship. These I planted like cannon and fitted them into frames that held them like a carriage, so that I could fire all the seven guns within two minutes. This wall I was many a weary month in finishing, and yet never thought myself safe till it was done.

When this was done, I stuck all the ground outside my wall, for a good distance in every direction, as full with stakes, or sticks, or the osier-like wood, which I found so apt to grow, as they could well stand, insomuch that I believe I might have set in near twenty thousand of them. I left a pretty large space between them and my wall that I might have room to see an enemy, and they might have no shelter from the young trees if they attempted to approach my outer wall.

Thus, in two years' time, I had a thick grove, and in five or six years' time I had a forest in front of my dwelling, growing so monstrous thick and strong that it was indeed completely impassable; and no men, of any kind at all, would ever imagine that there was anything beyond it, much less a habitation. As for the way in which I myself proposed to go in and out (for I left no avenue), it was by setting two ladders, one to a part of the rock which was low and had an indentation leaving room to place another ladder upon that. So when the two ladders were taken down, no man living could come down to me without doing himself mischief; and if they had come down, they were still on the outside of my outer wall. I was well and truly protected.

Thus I took all the measures human prudence could suggest for my own preservation; and it will be seen, later on, that they were not altogether without just reason, though I foresaw at that time nothing more than what mere fear suggested to me as the best course of action.

While this was going on, I was concerned also to secure the safety of my goats. For this purpose, after long consideration, I could think of but two ways to preserve them. One was to find another convenient place to dig a cave underground, and to drive them into it every night, and the other was to enclose two or three little bits of land, remote from one another, and as much concealed as I could, where I might keep about half a dozen young goats in each place. Then, if any disaster happened to the flock in general, I might be able to raise them again with a little trouble and time. The second idea, though it would require a great deal of time and work, I thought was the most rational plan and most fitting to my needs.

Accordingly, I spent some time finding the most

remote parts of the island, and I happened upon one which was as private, indeed, as my heart could wish for. It was a little, damp piece of ground in the middle of the hollow and thick woods, where I almost lost myself once before, while attempting to come back that way from the eastern part of the island. Here I found a clear piece of land, near three acres in size and so surrounded with woods that it was almost an enclosure by nature. At least, it did not need near so much effort to make it so as the other pieces of ground I had worked so hard at.

After I had thus secured one part of my little live-stock, I went around the whole island searching for another private place to make such another deposit. While wandering more to the west point of the island than I had ever done yet, and looking out to sea, I thought I saw a boat upon the sea, but at so great a distance that I could not be sure whether it was a boat or not.

When I came down the hill to the end of the island, where, indeed, I had never been before, I was soon convinced that seeing the print of a man's foot was not such a strange thing in the island as I imagined, and, except for the special providence that I had been cast upon the side of the island where the inhabitants never came, I would easily have known that nothing was more common than for the canoes from the mainland, when they happened to be too far out at sea, to shoot over to that side of the island for haven.

Likewise, as they often met and fought in their canoes, the victors having taken any prisoners, would bring them over to this shore, where, according to their dreadful customs, being all cannibals, they would kill and eat them; of which more later.

When I had come down the hill to the shore, as I said before, being the southwest point of the island, I was completely confounded and amazed at seeing the shore spread with skulls, hands, feet, and other bones of human bodies; and, particularly, I observed a place where there had been a fire made and a circle dug in the earth, like a cockpit, where I supposed the cannibals had sat down to their inhuman feastings upon the bodies of their poor unfortunate fellow creatures.

I was so astonished with the sight of these things that I forgot all about any danger to myself from it for a long while. All my apprehensions were buried in the thoughts of such a pitch of inhuman brutality and the horror of the degeneracy of human nature, which, though I had heard of it often, I had never yet had so near a view of before.

Going down to the seaside, I found a large tortoise (page 58)

I hung the grapes on the branches of trees (page 62)

Time, and the satisfaction I had that I was in no danger of being discovered by these people, began to wear off my uneasiness about them. I now began to live in just the same composed manner as before, only with this difference, that I used more caution, and kept my eyes open more widely than I did before, lest I should happen to be seen by any of them; and particularly, I was more cautious of firing my gun in case any of them, being on the island, should happen to hear its sound.

CHAPTER SEVEN
A SPANISH SHIP ASHORE

n this manner I continued quietly for nearly a year. I kept myself more inactive than ever, and seldom went from my cell except upon my constant employment: to milk my goats and manage my little flock in the woods, which, as it was on the other part of the island, was quite out of danger. For it is certain, that these people, who sometimes haunted this island, never came with any thoughts of finding anything here, and consequently never wandered off from the coast; and I doubt not but they might have been several times on shore after my awareness of them had made me cautious, as well as before.

I believe the reader of this will not think it strange if I confess that these anxieties, these constant dangers I lived in, and the concern that was now upon me, put an end to all invention, and to all the contrivances that I had laid for my future accommodations and conveniences.

I now had the care of my safety more upon my

hands than that of my food. I did not want to drive a nail or chop a stick of wood now for fear the noise I might make should be heard. Much less would I fire a gun, for the same reason. And above all, I was miserably uneasy at making any fire, lest the smoke, which is visible at a great distance in the day, should betray me.

For this reason, I moved that part of my business which required fire, such as making pots, pipes, and such, into my new apartment in the woods. There, after I had been some time, I found to my unspeakable consolation, a natural cave in the earth, which went in a vast way, and where, I dare say, no one, had he been at the mouth of it, would be so hardy as to venture in; nor, indeed, would any other man, but one who, like me, wanted nothing so much as a safe retreat.

While I was cutting down some wood here, I perceived that behind a very thick branch of low brushwood, or underwood, there was a kind of hollow place. I explored it and found myself in a cave. It was very small, that is to say, it might be about twelve feet, but in no manner of shape, neither round nor square, no hands having ever been employed in making it but those of Nature. I observed also that there was a place at the farther side of it that went in deeper, but was so low that it required me to creep upon my hands and knees to go into it, and whither it went I knew not. This seemed an unwise plan so, having no candle, I gave it over for that time, but resolved to come again the next day provided with candles and a tinderbox, which I had made of the lock of one of the muskets, with some wildfire in the pan.

Accordingly, the next day I came provided with six large candles of my own making (for I made very good candles now of goat's tallow, but was hard put for candlewick, using sometimes rags or rope yarn, and sometimes the dried rind of a reed-like nettle). Going into this low place, I was obliged to creep along on all fours, as I have said, almost ten yards, which, by the way, I thought was a very bold venture, considering that I knew not how far it might go, nor what was beyond it.

When I had made it through the strait, I found the roof rose higher up, I believe near twenty feet, and never was such a glorious sight seen in the island, I dare say, as it was to look round the sides and roof of this vault or cave. The wall reflected a hundred thousand lights to me from my two candles. What it was in the rock, whether diamonds or any other precious stones, or gold, which I rather supposed it to be, I could not possibly imagine.

The place I was in was a most delightful cavity or grotto of its kind, though perfectly dark, as could be expected. The floor was dry and level, and had a sort of small loose gravel upon it, so that there was no nauseous or venomous creature to be seen; neither was there any damp or wet on the sides or roof.

The only difficulty in it was the entrance, which, however, as it was a place of security, and such a retreat as I wanted, I thought it served my purpose. So, in all, I really rejoiced at the discovery, and resolved, without any delay, to bring some of those things which I was most anxious about to this place. Particularly, I resolved to bring hither my supply of powder and all my spare arms: two fowling pieces, for I had three in all, and three muskets, for of them I had eight in all. So I kept at my castle only five, which stood ready mounted like pieces of cannon on my outmost fence, as told before, and were ready also to take out upon any expedition. So I carried all away thither, never keeping above two or three pounds of powder with me in my castle, for fear of a surprise of any kind. I also carried over there all the lead I had left for bullets.

I now imagined myself like one of the ancient giants, which were said to live in caves and holes in the rocks, where none could come at them; for I persuaded myself, while I was here, that if five hundred cannibals were to hunt me, they could never find me; or, if they did, they would not venture to attack me here.

It was now the month of December in my twenty-third year of residence here; and this being the southern solstice (for winter I cannot call it), was the particular time of my harvest, and required my being much outside in the fields.

Going out pretty early in the morning, even before it was thorough daylight, I was surprised at seeing the light of some fire upon the shore, at a distance from me of about two miles, toward the end of the island where I had observed some cannibals had been as told before, and not on the other side, but, to my great affliction, it was on my side of the island.

I mounted to the top of the hill, and pulling out my spy-glass, which I had taken with me on purpose, I laid me down flat on the ground, and began to look for the place. I soon found there were no less than nine naked men sitting round a small fire, as I supposed, to cook some of their barbarous diet of human flesh.

They had two canoes with them, which they had hauled up upon the shore, and, as it was then an ebb tide, they seemed to me to wait for the return of the flood to go away again. It is not easy to imagine what confusion this sight put me into, especially seeing them on my side of the island, and so near me too.

When I considered their coming must be always with the current of the ebb, I began, afterward, to be more settled in my mind, being satisfied that I might go around with safety all the time of the tide of flood, if they were not on shore before; and having made this observation, I went about my harvest work with more composure and ease.

As I expected, so it proved. For, as soon as the tide made to the westward, I saw them all take to the boat and row (or paddle, as we call it) away. It was on the 16th of May that it blew a very great storm of wind all day, with a great deal of lightning and thunder, and a very foul night it was after it. I knew not what was the particular occasion of it, but as I was reading the Bible, and taken up with very serious thoughts about my present condition, I was surprised with the noise of a gun, as I thought, fired at sea. I immediately considered that this must be some ship in distress.

I had the presence of mind, at that minute, to think that, though I could not help them, it might be they might help me. So I brought together all the dry wood I could get at hand, and making a good handsome pile, I set it on fire upon the hill. I plied my fire all night long till daybreak; and when it was broad day, and the air cleared up, I saw something at a great distance at sea, full east of the island, whether a sail or a hull I could not distinguish, no, not even with my glass, the distance being so great, and the weather still something hazy also; at least it was there out at sea.

I looked frequently at it all that day, and soon perceived that it did not move, so I presently concluded that it was a ship at anchor; and being eager, you may be sure, to know, I took my gun in my hand and ran toward the south side of the island to the rocks; and getting up there, the weather by this time being perfectly clear, I could plainly see, to my great sorrow, the wreck of a ship, cast away in the night upon sunken rocks.

My mind was instantly filled with melancholy surmises about the fate of the crew, whether they had tried to make my island in their boat and had been swamped, or whether they had been carried out into the great ocean, where there was nothing but misery and death.

It was now calm, and I had a great mind to venture out in my boat to this wreck, not doubting but I might find something on board that might be useful to me; but that did not altogether interest me as much as the possibility that there might yet be some living creature on board whose life I might not only save, but might also, by saving that life, comfort my own to a great degree.

I resolved, the next morning, to set out with the first of the tide, and having slept the night in my canoe, I launched out. I went at a great rate directly for the wreck, and in less than two hours I came up to it. It was a dismal sight to look at: the ship, which, by the way it was built, was Spanish, stuck fast, jammed in between two rocks. All the stern and quarter of her were beaten to pieces by the sea, and as her forecastle, which stuck in the rocks, had run on with great violence, her mainmast and foremast were brought by the board, that is to say, broken short off; but her bowsprit was sound, and the head and bow appeared firm.

When I came close to the wreck, a dog appeared on the deck, and seeing me coming, yelped and cried; and as soon as I called him, he jumped into the sea to come to me. I took him into the boat, but found him almost dead with hunger and thirst. I gave him some of my bread and he devoured it like a ravenous wolf that had been starving two weeks or more in the snow. After this, I went on board. Beside the dog, there was nothing left in the ship that had life, nor any goods, that I could see, that were not spoiled by the water.

Upon the whole, I got very little by this voyage that was of any use to me.

CHAPTER EIGHT
MAN FRIDAY

bout a year and a half after the wreck of the Spanish ship, I was surprised early one morning, to see no less than five canoes all on shore together on my side of the island, and the people who belonged to them all landed and out of my sight.

I could not guess their number at all, for, knowing that they always came four or six or sometimes more in a boat, I could not tell what to think of it, or how to make any plans to attack twenty or thirty men singlehanded. So I lay still in my castle, perplexed and discomforted.

Having waited a good while, listening to hear if they made any noise, at length, being very impatient, I set my guns at the foot of my ladder, and clambered up to the top of the hill, by my two stages as usual, standing, however, so that my head did not appear above the hill, so that they could not perceive me by any means.

Here I observed, with the help of my spy-glass,

that they were no less than thirty in number, that they had a fire kindled, and that they had some meat. How they had cooked it I know not, or what it was, but they were all dancing round the fire making gestures and figures I could not make any sense of.

While I was thus looking on them, I perceived, by my perspective, two miserable wretches dragged from the boats, where, it seems, they were laid by, and were now brought out for the slaughter. I perceived one of them immediately fall, being knocked down, I suppose, with a club or wooden sword, for that was their way, and two or three others were at work immediately, getting him ready for their cookery, while the other victim was left standing by himself, till they should be ready for him. In that very moment, this poor wretch started away from them, and ran with incredible swiftness along the sands, directly toward me, I mean, toward that part of the coast where my habitation was.

I was dreadfully frightened, I must acknowledge, when I perceived him run my way, and especially when, as I thought, I saw him pursued by the whole group. However, I kept my station, and my spirits began to recover when I found that there were only three men that followed him; and still more was I encouraged when I found that he outstripped them exceedingly in running, and gained ground bit by bit, so that if he could but hold it for half an hour, he would fairly get away from them all easily, as I saw it.

Between them and my castle was the creek, where I landed my cargoes out of the ship, and this I saw plainly he must swim over, or the poor wretch would be taken there. But when the man escaping came thither, he made nothing of it, though the tide was then up. He plunged right in, swam through in about thirty stokes or thereabouts, landed, and ran on with exceeding strength and swiftness. When the three pursuers came to the creek, it happened that two of them could swim, but the third could not, and soon after went back again.

I observed that the two who swam were more than twice as long swimming over the creek than the fellow that was fleeing from them. It came very warmly upon my thoughts that now was the time to get me a servant, and perhaps a companion or assistant, and that I was called plainly by Providence to save this poor creature's life.

I immediately ran down the ladders with all possible expedition, fetched my two guns, for they were both at the foot of the ladders, and getting up again, with the same haste, to the top of the hill, I crossed toward the sea, and taking a very short cut, and all down hill, placed myself in the way between the pursuers and the pursued, hallooing aloud to him that fled, who, looking back, was at first, perhaps, as much frightened of me as of them; but I beckoned with my hand to him to come back, and, in the meantime, I slowly advanced toward the two that followed. Then, rushing at once upon the foremost, I knocked him down with the stock of my piece. I was loth to fire, because I did not want the rest of the men to hear.

Having knocked this fellow down, the other who pursued him stopped as if he had been frightened, and I advanced apace toward him. But as I came nearer, I soon perceived he had a bow and arrow and was fitting it to shoot at me. So I then had no choice but to shoot at him first, which I did, and killed him at the first shot. The poor native who fled had stopped, though he saw both his enemies fallen and killed, as he thought, yet was so frightened with the fire and noise of my piece that he stood stock still, and neither came forward nor went backward, though he seemed rather inclined to fly than to come near me.

I beckoned to him to come to me, and gave him all the signs of encouragement that I could think of; and he came nearer and nearer, kneeling down every ten or twelve steps in acknowledgement of my having saved his life. I smiled at him, and beckoned to him to come still nearer.

At length he came right up close, and then he kneeled down again, kissed the ground, and laid his head upon the ground, and taking me by the foot, set my foot upon his head. This, it seems, was in token of swearing to be my slave forever. I raised him, and made much of him, and encouraged him all I could.

But there was more work to do yet, for I perceived the pursuer whom I knocked down was not killed but stunned with the blow, and began to come to himself. So I pointed to him, and showed him that the other was not dead. Upon this he spoke some words to me, and though I could not understand them, yet I thought they were pleasant to hear, for they were the first sound of a man's voice that I had heard, my own excepted, for about twenty-five years. But there was no time for reflections now.

The man who was knocked down recovered himself so far as to sit up on the ground, and I perceived that my Indian began to be afraid; but when I saw that, I pointed my other piece at the man as if I would shoot him. Upon this, the man I was helping made a motion to me to lend him my sword which hung naked in a belt by my side, which I did.

He no sooner had it, but he ran to his enemy, and, at one blow, cut off his head so cleverly, no European executioner could have done it better; which I thought very strange for one who, I had reason to believe, never saw a sword in his life before, except their own wooden swords.

However, I learned afterward, that these people need to make their wooden swords so sharp, so heavy, and the wood is so hard, that they will cut off heads even with them, ay, and arms, and that at one blow too.

When he had done this, he came laughing to me, in sign of triumph, and brought me the sword again, and with many gestures which I did not understand, laid it down. But that which astonished him most was to know how I killed the other Indian so far off.

Pointing to the body, he made signs to me to let him go to look, so I bade him go. When he came to the man, he stood like one amazed, looking at him, turning him first on one side, then on the other, looking at the wound the bullet had made, which, it seems, was just in his breast. It had made a hole, but no great quantity of blood had followed, so he had bled inwardly, for he was quite dead.

He took up his bow and arrows and came back. So I turned to go away and beckoned him to follow me,

I made every kind of earthenware I needed (page 70)

It took me a month to shape it and dub it (page 72)

making signs to him that more might come after him. Upon this, he made signs to me that he would bury them in the sand, that they might not be seen by the rest if they followed; and so I made signs to him to do so.

He fell to work, and in an instant he had scraped a hole in the sand with his hands, big enough to bury the first in, and then dragged him into it, and covered him; and did so with the other also. I believe he had buried them both in a quarter of an hour. Then, calling him away, I conveyed him not to my castle, but to my cave on the farther part of the island. Here I gave him bread and a bunch of raisins to eat, and a draught of water, for which he was indeed in great distress because of his running; and having refreshed him, I made signs for him to go and lie down to sleep, showing him a place where I had laid some rice straw and a blanket, which I used to sleep upon myself sometimes.

So the poor creature lay down and immediately fell into a deep but brief sleep.

He was a comely, handsome fellow, perfectly well-made with straight, strong limbs, and slim, tall, and well-shaped, and, as I reckon, about twenty-six years of age. He had a very good countenance, not fierce nor surly, but seemed to have something very manly in his face; and yet he had all the sweetness and softness of a European in his countenance too, especially when he smiled.

His hair was long and black, not curled like wool; his forehead was high and large, and he had a great vivacity and sparkling sharpness in his eyes. The shade of his skin was not quite black, but very tawny; his face was round and plump; his nose small, not flat like the Africans; a very good mouth and thin lips and his fine teeth were well set, and as white as ivory.

After he had slumbered, rather than slept, about half an hour, he awoke again, and came out of the cave to me, for I had been milking my goats, which I had in the enclosure just by. When he espied me, he made all the signs to me of subjection, servitude, and submission imaginable, to let me know how he would serve me as long as he lived. I understood him in many things, and let him know I was very well pleased with him.

After we had spent some time together, I began to speak to him and teach him to speak to me, and first I let him know his name would be Friday, which was the day I saved his life. I called him so in memory of the time. I likewise taught him to say "Master", and then let him know that was to be my name. I likewise taught him to say "Yes" and "No", and to know their meaning. He seemed to learn very quickly.

I gave him some milk in an earthen pot, and let him see me drink it before him and soak my bread in it. I gave him a piece of bread to do the like, which he quickly complied with, and made signs that it was very good. I stayed there with him all that night, but as soon as it was day, I beckoned to him to come with me, and let him know that I would give him some clothes. He seemed very grateful, for he was stark naked.

As we went by the place where he had buried the two men, he pointed exactly to the spot, and showed me the marks he had made to find them again, making signs to me that we should dig them up again and eat them. At this I appeared very angry, expressed my abhorrence of it, and beckoned with my hand to come away, which he did immediately, with great submission.

I then led him up to the top of the hill to see if his enemies were gone. Pulling out my glass, I looked, and saw plainly the place where they had been, but saw no sign of them or their canoes, so it was plain that they were gone, and had left their two comrades behind them without any search after them.

Friday, by his signs, made me understand that they brought over four prisoners to feast upon; that three of them had been eaten up, and that he, pointing to himself, was the fourth; that there had been a great battle between them and their next king, whose subjects, it seems he had been one of. As well, they had taken a great number of prisoners, all of whom were carried to several places by those who had taken them in the fight, in order to feast upon them, as was done here by these cruel wretches from whom I had saved Friday.

I caused Friday to gather up all the skulls, bones, and flesh, and whatever remained, and lay them together in a heap, and make a great fire upon it, and burn them all to ashes so there was no sign left of this horrid event.

When he had done this, we came back to our castle, and there I fell to work for my man Friday. First of all, I gave him a pair of linen pantaloons, which I took out of the big locker or chest which I found in the wreck, and which, with a little alteration, fitted him very well; and then I made him a jerkin of goat's skin, as well as my skill would allow (for I had now become a fairly good tailor); and I gave him a good cap, which I made of hare's skin, very convenient and fashionable enough for us; and thus he was clothed for the present, tolerably well, and was mighty well pleased to see himself almost as stylish and well clothed as his master!

It is true, he moved awkwardly in those clothes at first: wearing the pantaloons was very strange to him, and the sleeves of the waistcoat pulled at his shoulders and the inside of his arms, but after I eased them a little where he complained that they hurt him, he began getting used to them, and finally took to them very well.

The next day after I came home to my hutch with him, I began to consider where I should lodge him that I might do well for him, and yet be perfectly easy in mind myself. However, I soon found that I need be under no apprehension on that score, for never man had a more faithful, loving, sincere servant than Friday was to me: without passions, sullenness, or designs, perfectly obliged and engaged, his very affections were tied to me like those of a child to a father; and I dare say he would have sacrificed his life to save mine upon any occasion whatsoever should the need arise. The many testimonies he gave me of this put me out of doubt, and soon convinced me that I needed to use no precautions as to my safety on his account.

I was greatly delighted with my new companion, and made it my business to teach him everything that was proper to make him useful, handy, and helpful, but especially to make him speak and understand me when I spoke; and he was the aptest scholar that ever was, and particularly was so merry, so constantly diligent, and so pleased when he could but understand me, or make me understand him, that it was very pleasant to me to talk to him. Now my life began to be so easy that I began to say to myself that, if I could but be safe from other Indians, I did not care if I were never to move from the place where I now lived.

After I had been two or three days back at my castle, I thought that, in order to change Friday from his horrid way of feeding, and from the relish of a cannibal's stomach, I ought to let him taste other flesh. So I took him out with me one morning to the woods. I went, indeed, intending to kill a kid out of my own flock, and bring it home and dress it, but as I was going, I saw a goat lying down in the shade, and two young kids sitting by her. I caught hold of Friday.

"Hold," said I; "stand still," and made signs to him not to stir.

Immediately I took my gun piece, shot, and killed one of the kids. Friday stood like one frightened, and I found he was the more amazed because he did not see me put anything into the gun, but thought that there must be some supernatural fund of death and destruction in that thing, able to kill man, beast, or bird, or anything near or far off; and the astonishment this created in him was such as would not wear off for a long time; and I believed, if I would have let him, he would have worshipped me and my gun.

As for the gun itself, he would not so much as touch it for several days after, but he would speak to it, and talk to it as if it had answered him, when he was by himself; which, as I afterward learned of him, was to beseech it not to kill him. I brought home the kid, and the same evening I took the skin off and prepared it as well as I could; and having a pot right for that purpose, I boiled or stewed some of the flesh and made some very good broth. After I had begun to eat some, I gave some to my man, who seemed very glad of it and liked it very much.

The next day I set him to work beating some corn out, and sifting it in the manner I used to do, as I observed before; and he soon understood how to do it as well as me, especially after he had seen what the meaning of it was, and that it was to make bread of it. For after that I let him see me make my bread and bake it too; and in a little time Friday was even willing and able to do all the work for me, as well as I could do it myself.

I began now to consider, that having two mouths to feed instead of one, I must provide more ground for my harvest and plant a larger quantity of corn than I used to do. So I marked out a larger piece of land and began the fence in the same manner as before, in which Friday worked not only very willingly and very hard, but did it very cheerfully. I then told him what it was for: that it was for corn to make more bread, because he was now with me, and that I might have enough for him and myself too. He appeared to understand that part, and let me know that he thought I now had much more work on his account than I had for myself, and that he would work the harder for me, if I would tell him what he needed to do.

This was the most pleasant year of all the life I led in this place. Friday began to talk pretty well, and to understand the names of almost everything I had occasion to call for, and of every place I had to send him to, and talked a great deal to me. So, in short, I now began to have some use for my tongue again, which, indeed, I had very little occasion for before, that is to say, about speech.

Beside the pleasure of talking to him, I had a singular satisfaction in the fellow himself: his simple, unfeigned honesty appeared to me more and more every day, and I began really to love this person; and, on his side, I believed he loved me more than it was possible for him ever to have loved anything before.

During the long time that Friday had been with me, I had been instructing him in the knowledge of the true God. I told him that the great Maker of all things lived up there, pointing up toward heaven; that He governed the world by the same power and providence by which He made it; and that He was omnipotent, and could do everything for us, give everything to us, take everything from us; and thus, by degrees, I opened his eyes.

He listened with great attention, and received with pleasure the notion of Jesus Christ being sent to redeem us, and of the manner of making our prayers to God, and His being able to hear us, even in heaven.

He told me one day, that if our God could hear us up beyond the sun, He must needs be a greater God than the god his tribe worshipped, Benamuckee, who lived but a little way off, and yet could not hear them till they went up to the great mountains where he dwelled to speak to him.

I had, God knows, more sincerity than knowledge in the methods I used for this poor creature's instruction, and must acknowledge that in teaching him, I really taught myself; so that, whether this poor wild wretch was the better for me or no, I had great reason to be thankful that ever he came to me.

My grief sat lighter upon me; my habitation grew comfortable to me beyond measure; and when I reflected, that in this solitary life which I had been confined to, I had not only been moved to look up to Heaven myself, and to seek the hand that had brought me here, but was now to be made an instrument, under Providence, to save the life, and, for ought I knew, the soul, of a non-believer, and bring him to the true knowledge of religion, and of the Christian doctrine, that he might know Christ Jesus, in whom is life eternal.

I say, when I reflected upon all these things, that a secret joy ran through every part of my soul, and I frequently rejoiced that I was brought to this deserted place, which I had so often thought the most dreadful of all afflictions that could possibly have befallen me.

CHAPTER NINE

RESCUE OF THE SPANISH PRISONER

fter Friday and I became more intimately acquainted, and he could understand almost all I said to him and speak pretty fluently to me, though in broken English, I acquainted him with my own history, or at least as much of it as related to my coming to this place.

I gave him an account of the wreck of which I had been on board, and showed him, as near as I could, the place where she lay; but she was all beaten to pieces by now, and gone. I showed him the ruins of our boat, which we lost when we escaped, and which I could not manage to move with my whole strength then; and which had now fallen almost to pieces and was quite useless.

Upon seeing this boat, Friday stood musing a long while, but said nothing. After a while, I asked him what it was he studied upon. At last, he says: "Me see such boat like come to place at my nation. We save the white mans from drown."

Then I asked him if there were any "white mans",

as he called them, in the boat.

"Yes," he said. "The boat full of white mans." I asked him how many. He told upon his fingers seventeen. I asked him then what became of them. He seemed to be thinking, then told me, "They live, they dwell at my nation."

Upon this, I inquired of him more fully what had become of them. He assured me they still lived there; that they had been there about four years; that the Indians let them alone and gave them victuals to live on. I asked him how it came to pass they did not kill them and eat them. He said, "No, they make brother with them." That is, as I understood him, a truce; and then he added, "They no eat mans but when make the war fight." That is to say, they never eat any men, only those who come to fight with them, and are taken in battle.

I now came to a decision to reach the territory of Friday's tribe, founded on the supposition gathered from our conversation that there were seventeen bearded men there. Therefore, without any more delay, I went to work with Friday to find a great tree proper to fell, and make a large periagua, or canoe, to undertake the voyage.

There were trees enough in the island to have built a little fleet, not of periaguas, or canoes, but even of good large vessels; but the main thing I tried to do was to get one so near the water that we might launch it when it was made, to avoid the mistake I committed at first. At last Friday decided upon a tree, for I found he knew much better than I what kind of wood was most suitable.

Friday was for burning the hollow or cavity out of the tree to make it into a boat, but I showed him how to cut it with tools, which, after I showed him how to use, he did very handily. After about a month, we finished it and made it very handsome, especially when, with our axes, which I showed him how to handle, we cut and hewed the outside into the true shape of a boat. After this, however, it took us nearly two weeks to get her along, as it were, inch by inch, upon great rollers into the water; but, when she was in, she would have carried twenty men with the greatest ease.

I took nearly two months rigging and fitting my mast and sails, for I made thorough work of it, making a small stay, and a sail or foresail to it, to assist, if we should turn to windward; and, most important of all, I fixed a rudder to the stern of her to steer with.

Later, when I came to teach Friday about the navigation of my boat, for though he knew very well how to paddle he knew nothing of the purpose of a sail or rudder, he was most amazed when he saw me work the boat in the sea by the rudder, and how the sail gibbed and filled this way or that way, as the course we sailed changed.

I was busy one morning upon the boat when I called to Friday and bid him go to the seashore and see if he could find a turtle, or tortoise, a thing we generally got once a week for the sake of the eggs as well as the flesh. Friday had not been long gone when he came running back and flew over my outer wall like one that felt not the ground or the steps he set his feet on; and before I had time to speak, he cried out to me, "O master! O master! O sorrow! O bad!"

"What's the matter, Friday?" says I.

"O yonder, there," says he, "one, two, three canoe: one, two, three!"

By this way of speaking I concluded there were six, but on inquiry I found he meant but three.

I made him take the two fowling pieces, which we always carried, and loaded them with large swan shot as big as small pistol bullets. Then I took four muskets and loaded them with two slugs, and five small bullets each; and my two pistols I loaded with a brace of bullets each. I hung my great sword, as usual, naked by my side, and gave Friday his hatchet so that he had some protection.

When I had thus prepared myself, I took my spy‑glass and went up to the top of the hill to see what I could discover; and I found quickly through my glass that there were one-and-twenty Indians, three prisoners, and three canoes; and that their whole business seemed to be the triumphant banquet upon these three prisoners' bodies. A barbarous feast indeed! But nothing more than, as I had observed, was unusual with them. I observed also that they had landed, not where they had when Friday made his escape, but nearer to my creek, where the shore was low, and where a thick wood came down close almost to the sea.

I divided the arms which I had charged, as before, between us. I gave Friday one pistol to stick in his girdle, and three guns upon his shoulder; and I took one pistol, and the other three guns myself; and in this posture we marched out. I charged Friday to keep close behind me and not to stir, or shoot, or do anything, till I bid him; and, in the meantime, not to speak a word. I fetched a compass to guide me for near a mile, as well to get over the creek as to get into the wood, so that I might come within shot of them before I should be discovered, which I had seen, by my glass, it was easy to do.

I dined like a king, attended by my servants (page 82)

I was surprised to see the print of a man's bare foot
(page 84)

I entered the woods, and with all possible wariness and silence, Friday followed close at my heels. I marched till I came to the edge of the woods, on the side which was next to them, but so that one corner of the woods lay between me and them. Here I called softly to Friday, and showing him a great tree, which was just at the corner of the woods, I bade him go to the tree and bring me word if he could plainly see from there what they were doing. He did so, and came immediately back to me, and told me they might be plainly viewed from there; that they were all sitting round their fire, eating the flesh of one of their prisoners, and that another lay bound upon the sand, a little from them, whom he said they would kill next, and which fired the very soul within me with a deep pity.

He told me the prisoner was not one of their nation, but one of the bearded men he told me of, that came to their country in the boat. I was filled with horror at the very naming of the bearded man, and going to the tree, I saw plainly by my glass a white man, who lay upon the beach of the sea with his hands and his feet tied with flags or rushes, and that he was a European and had clothes on.

There was another tree and a little thicket beyond it, about fifty yards nearer to them than the place where I was, which by going a little way around, I saw I might come at undiscovered, and that then I should be within half a shot of them. So I withheld my passion, though I was indeed enraged to the highest degree, and going back about twenty paces, I got behind some bushes, which gave cover all the way till I came to the other tree; and then came to a little rising ground, which gave me a full view of them at the distance of about eighty yards.

I now had not a moment to lose, for nineteen of the dreadful wretches sat upon the ground, all close-huddled together. They had just sent the other two to butcher the poor Christian, and were stooping down to untie the bands at his feet. I turned to Friday.

"Now, Friday," said I, "fire on them with your musket," which he did, and the same moment I fired also.

Friday took his aim so much better than I, that on the side that he shot, he killed two of them and wounded three more; and on my side, I killed one, and wounded two. They were, you may be sure, in dreadful consternation; and all of them who were not hurt jumped up on their feet, but did not immediately know which way to run, or which way to look, for they knew not from whence their destruction came. Then with my fowling piece I fired again among the amazed wretches, and so did Friday; and as our guns were now loaded with what I called swan shot, or small pistol bullets, we found only two drop, but so many were wounded that they ran about yelling and screaming like mad creatures, all bloody, and most of them miserably wounded, whereof three more fell quickly after, though I felt sure they were not quite dead.

Upon this I rushed out of the wood and showed myself, with Friday close at my heels. As soon as I perceived that they saw me, I shouted as loud as I could, and bade Friday do so too; and running as fast as I could, which by the way was not very fast, being loaded with arms as I was, I made directly towards the poor victim, who was, as I said, lying upon the beach between the place where they had sat and the sea, looking quite distraught.

The two butchers, who were just going to work on him, had left him at the surprise of our first fire, and fled in a terrible fright to the seaside, and had jumped into a canoe, and three more of the rest made off in the same way.

I turned to Friday and bade him step forward and fire at them. He understood me immediately, and running about forty yards to be nearer them, he shot at them, and I thought he had killed them all, for I saw them all fall of a heap into the boat, though I saw two of them get up again quickly. However, he killed two of them and wounded the third, so that he lay down in the bottom of the boat as though he were dead.

While my man Friday fired at them, I pulled out my knife and cut the ties that bound the poor victim, loosing his hands and feet; and when he stood up I thrust a pistol and sword into his hands. He took them very thankfully; and no sooner did he have the arms in his hands than, as if they had put a new strength into him, he flew upon his murderers like a fury, and had cut two of them in pieces in an instant. For the truth is, the whole attack was a surprise to them, and the poor creatures were so much frightened at the noise of our guns that they fell down from sheer amazement and fear, and had no more power to attempt their own escape than their flesh had to resist our shot. And that was the case of those five that Friday shot at in the boat, for as three of them fell with the hurt they had received, the other two fell with fright.

I kept my gun in my hand without firing, being willing to keep my charge ready, because I had given the Spaniard my pistol and sword. So I called to Friday, and bade him run up to the tree from whence we first fired and fetch the arms which lay there that had been discharged, which he did with great swiftness; and then giving him my musket, I sat down myself to load all the rest again, telling the other two to fetch them when needed.

Friday, now being free, pursued the flying wretches with no weapon in his hand but his hatchet; and with that he dispatched those three, who, as I said before, were wounded at first, and fallen, and all the rest he could come up with. When the Spaniard came to me for a gun, I gave him one of the fowling pieces, with which he pursued two of the cannibals and wounded them both, but as he was not able to run, they both got away from him into the wood, where Friday pursued them and killed one of them. But the other was too nimble for him, and though he was wounded, yet he plunged himself into the sea, and swam with all his might off to those who were left in the canoe. Those three in the canoe, with one wounded, and we know not whether he died or not, were all that escaped our hands of the one-and-twenty original men.

The account of all of them is as follows: three killed at our first shot from the tree; two killed at the next shot; two killed by Friday in the boat; two killed by Friday of those at first wounded; one killed by Friday in the woods; three killed by the Spaniard, the two I have mentioned and a third whom he shot with my pistol afterward; four killed, being found dropped here and there of their wounds or killed by Friday in his chase of them; four escaped in the boat, whereof one was wounded if not dead. Twenty-one in all.

Those who were in the canoe worked hard to get out of gunshot, and though Friday took two or three shots at them, I did not find that he hit any of them. So, running to one of their canoes, I jumped in and bade Friday follow me; but I was surprised to find another poor creature there, bound hand and foot for the slaughter and almost dead with fear, not knowing what was the matter; for he had not been able to look up over the side of the boat. But when Friday came to hear him speak, and look in his face, it would have moved anyone to tears to have seen how Friday kissed him, embraced him, hugged him, cried, laughed, halloed, jumped about, danced, sung; then cried again, wrung his hands, beat his own face and head; and then sang and jumped about again, like a distracted creature.

It was a good while before I could make him speak to me or tell me what was the matter, but when he came to himself a little, he told me that it was his father.

This affair put an end to our pursuit of the canoe with the other cannibals, who were now almost out of sight; and it was happy for us that we did not, for it blew so hard within two hours after, and before they could have got a quarter of their way, and continued blowing so hard all night, and that from the northwest, which was against them, that I could not suppose that their boat could last, or that they ever reached their own coast.

Friday now came out of the boat and ran home for an earthen jug to bring his father some fresh water, which revived him wonderfully, for he was fainting with thirst.

As soon as I had settled my two weak, rescued prisoners and given them shelter and a place to rest themselves, I began to think of preparing a meal for them, and made them a very good dish, I assure you, of the flesh of a yearling goat with broth, having put some barley and rice also into the broth.

I carried it all into the new tent, and having set a table for them, I sat down and also ate my dinner with them, and, as well as I could, cheered them and encouraged them. Friday was my interpreter, especially for his father, and, indeed, for the Spaniard too, for the Spaniard spoke the language of the Indians pretty well. Then I asked Friday to inquire

of his father what treatment we were likely to receive
of his people if we carried out my project of escape,
and was assured by Friday's father that I might
depend upon good usage from their nation, on his
account, if I would go.

But my thoughts were a little suspended when I
had a serious discourse with the Spaniard, and when
I understood that there were sixteen more of his
countrymen and Portuguese, who, having been cast
away and made their escape to that side, lived there
at peace, indeed, with the Indians, but were very sore
put to it for necessities, and still feared for their lives.

I asked him all the particulars of their voyage and
found that they had five Portuguese seamen on
board, whom they took out of another wreck; that
five of their own men were drowned when first the
ship was lost, and that these escaped through infinite
dangers and hazards and arrived, almost starved, on
the cannibal coast, where they expected to have been
devoured every moment. He told me they had some
arms with them, but they were perfectly useless, for
they had neither powder nor ball, the washing of the
sea having spoiled all their powder, except for a small
amount, which they used at their first landing to
provide themselves some food.

Upon these assurances, I resolved to venture to

rescue them, if possible, and to send Friday's father and this Spaniard over to them to bargain. But when we had got all things in readiness to go, the Spaniard stated an objection, which had so much prudence in it, on one hand, and so much sincerity, on the other hand, that I could not but be very well satisfied in it; and, by his advice, put off the deliverance of his comrades for at least half a year.

He told me he thought it would be more advisable to let him and the other two dig and cultivate some more land, as much as I could spare seed to sow, and that we should reap another harvest, that we might have a supply of corn for his countrymen when they should come; for need might be a temptation to them to disagree, or to think themselves undelivered by going out of one difficulty into another. So we fell to digging, all four of us, as well as the wooden tools we were furnished with permitted; and in a month's time, by the end of which it was seedtime, we had so much land cured and trimmed and prepared that we sowed two and twenty bushels of barley and sixteen jars of rice.

At the same time, I contrived to increase my little flock of tame goats as much as I could. But, above all, the season for curing the grapes coming on, I caused such a prodigious quantity to be hung up in the sun, that, I believe, had we been at Alicante, where the grapes are cured in the same way, we could have filled sixty or eighty barrels; and these, with our bread, was a great part of our food, and was very good too, I can assure you, for it is exceedingly nourishing.

It was now harvest and our crop in good order. It was not the most plentiful increase I had seen in the island, but it was enough to answer our needs for, from twenty-two bushels of barley, we brought in and threshed out over two hundred and twenty bushels, and the like in proportion of the rice — enough to last us through a good year.

And now, having a full supply of food for all the guests I expected, I gave the Spaniard leave to go over to the mainland, to see what he could do with those he had left behind him there. The Spaniard and the old Indian, the father of Friday, went away in one of the canoes in which they were brought as prisoners.

I gave each of them a musket with a firelock on it, and about eight charges of powder and ball, charging them to be very good guardians of both, and not to use either of them except when urgently necessary. They went away with a fair gale on the day that the moon was full, which, by my account, must have been in the month of October.

Eight days after their departure I was fast asleep in my hutch one morning when my man Friday came running in to me and called aloud, "Master, master, they are come, they are come!"

I jumped up, but I was surprised, when turning my eyes to the sea, to observe a boat about a league and a half distance, standing in for the shore, with a shoulder-of-mutton sail, as they call it, and the wind blowing fair to bring them in. Also, I soon observed that they did not come from that side which the shore lay on, but from the southernmost end of the island. Upon this, I went in to fetch my spy-glass, and using it from the top of the hill plainly discovered a ship lying at anchor, at about two leagues and a half distance from me, south south east, but not above a league and a half from the shore.

By my observation, it appeared plainly to be an English ship, and the boat appeared to be an English longboat.

I cannot express the confusion I was in. In the first place, it occurred to me to consider what business an English ship could have in that part of the world, since it was not the way to or from any part of the world where the English had any traffic; and I knew there had been no storms to drive them in there, as in distress; and that if they were really English, it was most probably that they were here for no good purpose; and that I had better continue as I was, rather than fall into the hands of thieves and murderers.

I had not been long in this position when I saw the boat on shore upon the beach, about half a mile from me. When they were on the shore, I was fully satisfied they were Englishmen.

There were eleven men in all whereof three I saw were unarmed, and, as I thought, bound; and when the first four or five of them had jumped on shore, they took those three out of the boat as prisoners.

One of the three men I could perceive was using the most passionate gestures of entreaty, affliction, and despair, even to a kind of extravagance. The other two, I could perceive, lifted up their hands sometimes, and appeared concerned, indeed, but not to such a degree.

After I had noticed the outrageous usage of the three men by the insolent seamen, I observed the fellows run scattering about the island with great enthusiasm, as if they wanted to see the country. I found that the three other men had liberty to go also where they pleased; but they sat down on the ground, very pensive, and looked like men in despair.

CHAPTER TEN

THE MUTINY

t was just at the top of high tide when these people came on shore, and while they rambled around to see what kind of a place they were in, they had carelessly stayed till the tide was spent and the water had ebbed away enough to leave their boat aground. They had left two men in the boat, who, as I found afterward, having drunk a little too much brandy, fell asleep.

For a while I kept very close to home, not once daring to stir out of my castle any farther than to my place of observation near the top of the hill; and very glad I was to think how well it was fortified. I knew it was no less than ten hours before the boat could float again, and by that time it would be dark, and I might be at more liberty to see their motions and to hear their discourse, if they had any.

In the meantime, I fitted myself up for the battle. I took two fowling pieces and I gave Friday three muskets. My appearance, indeed, was very fierce. I had my formidable goatskin coat on, with the great cap I have mentioned, a naked sword by my side, two pistols in my belt, and a gun upon each shoulder.

It was my plan, as I said before, not to make a move till it was dark; but about two o'clock, being the heat of the day, I found that they were all gone straggling into the woods, and as I thought, laid down to sleep. The three poor distressed men, too anxious for their lives to get any sleep, were, however, sitting under the shelter of a large tree about a quarter of a mile from me, and, as I thought, out of sight of any of the rest. Upon this I resolved to show myself to them and learn something of their condition.

Immediately I marched toward them, my man Friday at a good distance behind me, as formidable for his arms as I, but not making quite so frightening a ghost-like figure as I did. I came as near to them as I could unseen, and then, before any of them saw me, I called aloud to them in Spanish, "What are ye, gentlemen?"

They started at the noise, but were ten times more confounded when they saw me, and the uncouth figure I made. They made no answer at all, but I thought I perceived them just going to fly from me, when I spoke to them in English:

"Gentlemen, I am an Englishman, and disposed to

assist you. You see I have one servant only. We have arms and ammunition. Tell us freely, can we serve you? What is your case?"

"Our case," said one, "sir, is too long to tell you while our murderers are so near us; but, in short, sir, I was commander of that ship and my men have mutinied against me. They have been prevailed on not to murder me, and at last have set me on shore in this desolate place with these two men with me, one my mate, the other a passenger, where we expected to perish, believing the place to be uninhabited, and know not yet what to think of it."

"Where are these brutes, your enemies?" said I. "Do you know where they have gone?"

"There they lie, sir," said he, pointing to a thicket of trees. "My heart trembles for fear they have seen us, and heard you speak. If they have, they will certainly murder us all."

"Have they any firearms?" said I.

He answered, "They had only two guns, one of which they left in the boat."

"Well, then," said I, "leave the rest to me. I see they are all asleep; it is an easy thing to kill them all; but shall we rather take them prisoners?"

He told me there were two desperate villains among them to whom it was not safe to show any

The roof was, I believe, about twenty feet high (page 96)

There were no less than nine naked men sitting round a fire
(page 98)

mercy, but if they were secured, he believed all the rest would return to their duty. I asked him which they were. He told me he could not distinguish them at a distance, but he would obey my orders in anything I would direct.

"Well," says I, "let us retreat out of their view or hearing, lest they awake, and we will plan further." So they willingly went back with me, till the woods safely covered us from them.

"Look you, sir," said I, "if I venture upon your deliverance, are you willing to make two conditions with me? First, that while you stay on this island with me, you will not try to take any authority here, and be governed by my orders; secondly, that if the ship is recovered, you will carry me and my man to England, passage free."

He gave me all the assurances that the invention or faith of man could devise. "Well, then," said I, "here are three muskets for you, with powder and ball. Tell me what you think is proper to be done next."

He said, very modestly, that he was loth to kill the mutineers if he could help it; but that those two were incorrigible villains, and had been the authors of the mutiny in the ship, and if they escaped, we would be undone, for they would go on board and bring the whole ship's company and destroy us all.

In the middle of this discourse, we heard some of them awake, and soon after we saw two of them on their feet. I asked him if either of them were the heads of the mutiny. He said they were not.

"Well, then," said I, "you may let them escape, and Providence seems to have awakened them on purpose to save themselves. Now," said I, "if the rest escape you, it is your fault."

Animated with this, he took the musket I had given him in his hand, and a pistol in his belt, and his two comrades with him, each with a gun in his hand. The two men who were with him went first and made some noise, at which one of the seamen who was awake turned round and, seeing them coming, cried out to the rest; but it was too late, for the moment he cried out they fired. I mean the two men, the captain wisely reserving his own gun. They had so well aimed their shot at the men they knew, that one of them was killed on the spot, and the other very much wounded; but not being dead, he started up on his feet, and called eagerly for help to the others; but the captain knocked him down with the stock of his musket so that he never spoke more. But there were three more in the company, and one of them was also slightly wounded.

By this time I had come, and when they saw their

danger, and that it was in vain to resist, they begged for mercy. The captain told them he would spare their lives if they would swear to be faithful to him in recovering the ship, and afterward in carrying her back to Jamaica, from whence they came. They gave him all the protestations of their sincerity that could be desired, and he was willing to believe them and spare their lives, which I was not against, only that I obliged him to keep them bound hand and foot while they were on the island.

While this was happening, I sent Friday with the captain's mate to the boat, with orders to secure her and bring away the oars and sails, which they did; and by and by three straggling men that were (happily for them) parted from the rest, came back upon hearing the guns fired, and seeing the captain, who before was their prisoner, now their conqueror, submitted to be bound also. And so our victory was complete.

I told the captain the first thing we had to do was to scuttle the boat which lay upon the beach, so that they might not carry her off. We needed to take everything out of her, and leave her so far useless as not to be fit to float. Accordingly we went on board and took the arms which were left, and whatever else of use we found there.

Then we knocked a hole in her bottom so that, if they proved strong enough to master us, yet they could not carry off the boat.

While we were musing what we should do, we heard the ship fire a gun and saw her make a wave with her ensign as a signal for the boat to come on board. But no boat stirred, so they fired several times, making other signals for the boat. At last, when all their signals and firing proved fruitless and they found the boat did not stir, we saw them, with the help of my glasses, hoist another boat out and row toward the shore; and we found, as they approached, that there were no less than ten men in her, and that they had firearms with them.

As the ship lay almost two leagues from the shore, we had a full view of them as they came, and the captain knew the names and characters of all the men in the boat, of whom he said there were three very honest fellows, who, he was sure, were led into this conspiracy by the rest, being overpowered and frightened. As for the boatswain, who, it seems, was the chief officer among them, and all the rest, they were as outrageous as any of the ship's crew, and were no doubt made desperate in their new enterprise; and he was terribly apprehensive that they would be too powerful for us.

We had, upon the first appearance of the boat's coming from the ship, decided to send away our prisoners, as we had, indeed, secured them effectually. Two of them, of whom the captain was less sure of than the others, I sent with Friday, and one of the three delivered men, to my cave.

Of the other prisoners, two of them were kept pinioned because the captain could not trust them; but the other two were taken into my service, upon the captain's recommendation and upon their solemnly engaging to live and die with us. So with them and the three honest men, we were seven men well armed; and I made no doubt we should be able to deal well enough with the ten that were coming, considering that the captain had said that there were three or four honest men among them also. As soon as they got to the place where their other boat lay, they ran their boat onto the beach and came on shore, hauling the boat up after them.

Once on shore, the first thing they did was to run to their other boat; and it was easy to see they were greatly surprised to find her stripped, as above, of all that was in her, and a huge hole in her bottom. After they had mused awhile upon this, they set up two or three great shouts, hallooing with all their might, to see if they could make their companions hear, but their shouts were to no purpose. Then they came all close together in a ring and fired a volley of shots from their small arms. They were so astonished at getting no reply to this that they immediately launched their boat again and all of them got on board.

They had not long put off in the boat than we saw them all coming on shore again, but with this new measure in their conduct, which it seems they consulted together upon: to leave three men in the boat, and the rest to go on shore and into the woods to look for their fellows. This was a great disappointment to us, for now we were at a loss what to do, as our seizing those seven men on shore would be no advantage to us if we let the boat escape, because they would then row to the ship, and then the rest of them would be sure to weigh anchor and set sail, and so our chance to recover the ship would be lost. However, we had no remedy but to wait and see what might happen.

The seven men came on shore, and the three who remained in the boat put her off to a good distance from the shore and came to anchor to wait for them, so that it was impossible for us to reach them in the boat. Those who came on shore kept close together, marching toward the top of the little hill under which my habitation lay; and we could see them plainly, though they could not perceive us. We would have been very glad if they would have come nearer to us, so that we might have fired at them, or that they would have gone farther off, that we might have come out.

When they had come to the brow of the hill, where they could see a great way into the valleys and woods, which lay toward the northeast part and where the island lay lowest, they shouted and hallooed till they were weary; and not caring, it seems, to venture far from the shore, not far from one another, they sat down together under a tree, to consider what to do next. Had they thought fit to have gone to sleep there, as the other group of them had done, they would have done the job for us; but they were too full of apprehensions of danger to venture going to sleep, though they could not tell what the danger was they had to fear.

We waited a long while, though very impatient for them to go away, and were very uneasy, when, after long consultations, we saw them all get up and march towards the sea. It seems they had such dreadful apprehensions upon them of the danger of the place, that they resolved to go on board the ship again, give their companions over for lost, and so go on with their intended voyage with the ship.

As soon as I saw them go towards the shore, I thought of a stratagem to fetch them back again, and which answered my end perfectly. I ordered Friday and the captain's mate to go over the little creek westward, toward the place where the Indians came on shore when Friday was rescued, and as soon as they came to a little rising ground about half a mile distant, I bade them halloo out, as loud as they could, and wait till they were sure the seamen heard them. Then, as soon as ever they heard the seamen answer them, they should return it again; and then keeping out of sight, move away, always answering when the others hallooed, to draw them as far into the island and among the woods as possible, and then wheel around and come again to me, by such a route as I directed them.

They were just going into the boat when Friday and the mate hallooed. They soon heard them, and answering, ran along the shore westward toward the voices they heard, when they were stopped by the creek, where the water being high, they could not get over, and called for the boat to come up and carry them over, as I expected.

When they had moved themselves over, I observed that the boat, being a good way into the creek and, as it were, in a port within the land, they took one of the three men out of her to go along with them, and left only two in the boat, having fastened her to the stump of a little tree on the shore. This was what I wished for, and immediately leaving Friday and the captain's mate to their business, I took the rest with me, and crossing the creek out of sight, we surprised the two men before they were aware: one of them lying on the shore, and the other being in the boat.

The fellow on shore was between sleeping and waking, and the captain, who was foremost, ran in upon him and knocked him down, and then called out to the one in the boat to surrender or he was a dead man. Very few arguments were needed to persuade a single man to surrender, when he saw five men upon him and his comrade knocked down. Beside, this was, it seems, one of the three who were not so hearty in the mutiny as the rest of the crew, and therefore was easily persuaded not only to surrender, but afterward to join sincerely with us. In the meantime, Friday and the captain's mate so well managed their business with the rest of the men, that they drew them, by hallooing and answering, from one hill to another, and from one wood to another, till they not only heartily tired them, but left them where they were, very sure they could not get back to the boat before it was dark; and, indeed, they were heartily tired themselves by the time they came back to us.

We had nothing to do now but to watch for them in the dark and to fall upon them, so as to make sure work of them. It was several hours after Friday came back to me before they came back to their boat, and we could hear the one in front, long before they came right up, calling to those behind to come along; and could also hear them answer and complain how lame and tired they were, and not able to come any faster, which was very welcome news to us. At length, they came up to the boat, but it is impossible to describe their confusion when they found the boat fast aground in the creek, the tide ebbed out, and their two men gone.

I resolved to wait, to see if they did not separate, and, therefore, to make sure of them, I drew my ambuscade nearer, and ordered Friday and the captain to creep upon their hands and feet as close to the ground as they could, that they might not be discovered, and get as near them as they possibly could before they began to fire.

They had not been long in that work when the boatswain, who was the principal ringleader of the mutiny and had now shown himself the most dejected and dispirited of all, came walking toward them with two more of the crew. The captain was so eager at having this principal rogue so much in his power that he could hardly have patience to let him come near enough so as to be sure of him, for they only heard his tongue before; but when they came nearer, the captain and Friday, jumping to their feet, let fly at them.

The boatswain was killed on the spot. The next man was shot in the body and fell just by him, though he did not die till an hour or two after. The third ran for it. At the noise of the fire, I immediately advanced with my whole army, which was now eight men: myself, generalissimo, Friday, my lieutenant-general; the captain and his two men, and the three prisoners of war, whom we had trusted with arms. We came upon them in the dark so that they could not see our number, and I made the man they had left in the boat, who was now one of us, call to them by name, to try to bring them to a discussion, and so perhaps reduce them to terms.

So he calls out as loud as he could to one of them, "Tom Smith! Tom Smith!"

He answered immediately, "Is that Robinson?", for it seemed he knew the voice.

The other answered, "Ay, ay. For God's sake,

Tom Smith, throw down your arms and yield, or you are all dead men this moment."

"Who must we yield to? Where are they?" says Smith.

"Here they are," says he. "Our captain and fifty men have been hunting you these two hours. The boatswain is killed, Will Fry is wounded, and I am a prisoner; and if you do not yield, you are all lost."

"Will they give us quarter then?" says Tom Smith. "If yes, we will yield."

"I will go and ask, if you promise to yield," says Robinson.

So he asked the captain, and the captain himself then called out, "You, Smith, you know my voice. If you lay down your arms immediately and submit, you shall have your lives, all but Will Atkins."

They all laid down their arms and begged for their lives, and I sent the man that had talked with them, and two more, who bound them all; and then my great army of fifty men, which with those three, were in all but eight, came up and seized them and their boat. But I kept myself and one more out of sight for reasons of state.

Our next work was to repair the boat and plan how to seize the ship. As for the captain, he told the mutineers that they were not really his prisoners, but the commander's of the island, who was an English-man; that he might hang them all there, if he pleased, but as he had given them all quarter, he supposed he would send them all to England, to be dealt with there as justice required, except Atkins, whom he was commanded by the governor to advise to prepare for death, for he would be hanged at first light in the morning.

Though all this was but a fiction of his own making, it, indeed, had the desired effect. Atkins fell upon his knees to beg the captain to intercede with the governor for his life, and all the rest begged him, for God's sake, not to send them back to England.

All this time I was careful to keep in the dark that they might not see what sort of a governor I was. Upon the captain coming to me, I told him we must divide the prisoners, and then he should go and take Atkins and two more of the worst of them, and send them pinioned to the cave where the others lay. The rest I ordered to be taken to my bower.

I sent the captain to these men in the morning. He told them that, though the governor had given them quarter for their lives as to the present action, yet if they were sent to England, they would all be hanged in chains, to be sure; but that if they would join in the just attempt to recover the ship, he would have the governor's guarantee for their pardon.

Anyone may guess how readily such a proposal would be accepted by men in their condition. They fell down on their knees to the captain and promised, with the deepest oaths, that they would be faithful to him to the last.

"Well," says the captain, "I must go and tell the governor what you say, and see what I can do to bring him to consent to it."

So he brought me an account of the temper he had found them in, and that he verily believed they would be faithful. However, that we might be very certain I told him he should go back again and choose five, and tell them that they might see he did not need men, that he would take out those five to be his assistants, and that the governor would keep the other two and the three that were sent prisoners to the castle (my cave) as hostages for the fidelity of those five; and that if they proved unfaithful in execution, the five hostages would be hanged in chains on the shore.

Our forces were now thus arranged for the expedition: first the captain, his mate, and passenger; second, the two prisoners of the first gang, to whom, having their character from the captain, I had given their liberty and trusted them with arms; third, the other two that I had kept till now in my bower, pinioned, but, on the captain's motion, now released; fourth, these five last released; so that there were twelve in all, beside five we kept prisoners in the cave for hostages.

The captain now had no difficulties except to furnish his two boats, stop the breach of one, and man them. He made his passenger captain of one, with four of the men, and he himself, his mate, and five more went in the other; and they managed very well, for they came up to the ship about midnight.

As soon as they came within call of the ship, he made Robinson hail them and tell them they had brought off the men and the boat, but that it was a long time before they had found them, and the like, holding them in conversation till they came to the ship's side.

Then the captain and the mate, entering first with their arms, immediately knocked down the second mate and carpenter with the butt end of their muskets. Being very faithfully seconded by their men, they bound all the rest that were upon the main and quarter decks, and began to fasten the hatches to keep those who were below secured. Then the other boat and their men, entering at the forechains, secured the forecastle of the ship and the scuttle, which went down into the kitchen, making three men they found there prisoners.

When this was done, and all were safe upon deck, the captain ordered the mate and three men to break into the roundhouse, where the new rebel captain lay, who having heard the alarm, had got up, and with two men and a boy had taken firearms; and when the mate, with a crowbar, split open the door, the new captain and his men fired boldly among them, and wounded the mate with a musket ball, which broke his arm and wounded two more of the men, but killed nobody.

The mate called for help, but rushed into the roundhouse, wounded as he was, and with his pistol shot the new captain through the head, upon which the rest yielded, and the ship was taken effectually, without any more lives lost.

As soon as the ship was thus recovered, the captain ordered seven guns to be fired, which was the signal agreed upon to give me notice of his success, which you may be sure I was very glad to hear, having sat watching upon the shore for it till near two o'clock in the morning. As soon as it was light, the captain came ashore in the pinnace, bringing as a present to me six new clean shirts, six very good neckcloths, two pairs of gloves, one pair of shoes, a hat and one pair

The Spanish ship was stuck fast between two rocks
(page 101)

He was amazed when he saw me use the rudder
(page 125)

of stockings, with a very good suit of clothes of his own, which had been worn very little; in a word, he clothed me from head to foot. It was a very kind and agreeable present, as anyone may imagine, to one in my circumstances, but never was anything in the world of that kind so unpleasant, awkward, and uneasy, as it was to me to wear such clothes for the first few days.

As soon as I was dressed in my new habit, I caused Friday and the two hostages (for they were now discharged, their comrades having performed their promise) to go to the cave and bring up the five men, pinioned as they were, to the bower and keep them there till I came. Being all met, and the captain with me, I caused the men to be brought before me, and I told them that by my direction the ship had been seized; that she lay now in the road; that they might see by and by that their new captain had received the reward of his villainy, and that they would see him hanging at the yard arm. As for them, I wanted to know why they thought I should not execute them as pirates, taken in the fact, unless they had a mind to take their fate on the island. If they desired that, as I had liberty to leave the island, I had some inclination to give them their lives, if they thought they could shift on shore. They seemed very thankful for it, and said they would much rather venture to stay there than be carried to England to be hanged. So I left it on that issue.

When they had all declared their willingness to stay, I then told them I would tell them the story of my living there, and put them into the way of making it easy for themselves. Accordingly, I gave them the whole story of the place and of my coming to it; showed them my fortifications, the way I made my bread, planted my corn, cured my grapes; and, in a word, all that was necessary to make life easy. I told them the story also of the seventeen Spaniards that were to be expected, for whom I left a letter, and made them promise to treat them in common with themselves.

They appeared very thankful, and I accordingly set them at liberty, and bade them retire into the woods to the place whence they came, and I would leave them some firearms, some ammunition, some provisions, and some directions on how they could live very well, if they thought fit.

I left them my firearms: five muskets, three fowling pieces, and three swords. I had over a barrel and a half of powder left, for after the first year or two I used but little, and wasted none. I gave them a description of the way I managed the goats, and directions to milk and fatten them, and to make both butter and cheese; in a word, I gave them every part of my own story, and told them I should prevail with the captain to leave them two more barrels of gunpowder and some garden seeds, which I told them I would have been very glad of; also I gave them a bag of peas which the captain has brought me to eat, and bade them be sure to sow and increase them.

Having done all this, I left them the next day and went on board the ship. We prepared immediately to sail, but did not weigh anchor that night.

The next morning early, two of the five men came swimming to the ship's side, and making a most lamentable complaint of the other three, begged to be taken into the ship, for God's sake, for they should be murdered, and begged the captain to take them on board, even if he hanged them immediately. Upon this the captain pretended to have no power without me; but after some difficulty, and after their solemn promises of amendment, they were taken on board, and were some time after soundly whipped, after which they proved very honest and quiet fellows.

Some time after this, the boat was ordered on shore, the tide being up, with the things promised to the men, to which the captain, at my intercession, caused their chests and clothes to be added, which they took, and were very thankful for. I also encouraged them by telling them that if it lay in my power to send any vessel to take them in, I would not forget them.

When I took leave of this island, I carried on board, for relics, the great goatskin cap I had made, my umbrella, and one of my parrots; also I forgot not to take the money I formerly mentioned, which had lain by me so long useless that it had grown rusty or tarnished, and could hardly pass for silver, till it had been a little rubbed and handled, and began to look like new, and also some money I found in the wreck of the Spanish ship.

Thus I left the island on the 19th of December in the year 1686, as I found by the ship's account, after I had been upon it eight-and-twenty years, two months, and nineteen days, being delivered from this second captivity the same day of the month that I first made my escape in the longboat from among the Moors of Sallé.

In this vessel, after a long voyage, I arrived in England on the 11th of June, in the year 1687, having been thirty-five years absent.

CHAPTER ELEVEN
CRUSOE GOES HOME

When I came to England, I was as perfect a stranger to all the world as if I had never been known there. I went down into Yorkshire, but my father and mother were dead, and all the family unknown, except that I found two sisters and two of the children of one of my brothers. As I had been long ago given up for dead, there had been no provision made for me, so that, in a word, I found nothing to relieve me or assist me. The little money I had would not do much for me toward settling in the world.

I met with one piece of gratitude which I did not expect. This was, that the master of the ship whom I so happily delivered, and by the same means saved the ship and cargo, having given a very handsome account to the owners of the manner in which I had saved the lives of the men and the ship, invited me to meet them and some other merchants concerned, and all together made me a very handsome compliment upon the subject, and a present of almost two hundred pounds sterling to add to my savings.

I resolved to go to Lisbon and see if I might not come by some information of the state of my plantation in Brazil. With this view, I took ship for Lisbon, where I arrived in the April following, my man Friday accompanying me very faithfully in all these ramblings, and proving a most honest servant upon all occasions. When I came to Lisbon, I sought out my old friend, the captain of the ship who first took me to sea off the shore of Africa. He had now grown old, and had left off going to sea, having put his son into his ship, who still plied the Brazil trade.

After some passionate expressions of the old acquaintance between us, I inquired, you may be sure, after my plantation and my partner. The old man told me he had not been in Brazil for about nine years, but he could assure me that when he came away my partner was living, but the trustees, whom I had joined with him to take cognizance of my part, were both dead.

However, he believed I would have a very good account of the improvement of the plantation, for, on the general belief of my being cast away and drowned, my trustees had given in the account of the produce of my part of the plantation to the procurator-fiscal, who had appropriated it, in case I never came to claim it, one-third to the king and two-thirds to the monastery of St. Augustine, to be expended for the benefit of the poor and for the conversion of the Indians to the Catholic faith; but that if I appeared, or anyone for me, to claim the inheritance, it would be restored, except that the improvement, or annual production, being distributed to charitable uses, could not be.

"But," says the old man, "I have one piece of news to tell you, which, perhaps, may not be so acceptable to you as the rest; and that is, believing you were lost, and all the world believing so also, your partner and trustees did offer to account with me, in your name, for six or eight of the first years of profit, which I received."

The old man then told me that he was in debt to me for four hundred and seventy moidores of gold, besides sixty chests of sugar and fifteen double rolls of tobacco, which were lost in his ship, when he was shipwrecked coming home to Lisbon about eleven years after my leaving the place. The good man then began to complain of his misfortunes, and how he had been obliged to make use of my money to recover his losses and buy him a share in a new ship.

"However, my old friend," says he "you shall not be out of fortune through my owing you, and as soon as my son returns, you shall be fully satisfied." Upon this, he pulls out an old pouch and gives me one hundred and sixty Portugal moidores in gold; and taking the writings of his title to the ship, in which his son had gone to Brazil, and of which he was a quarter part owner and his son another, he put them both into my hands, to be security for the rest.

I was too much moved with the honesty and kindness of the poor man to be able to bear this, and remembering what he had done for me, how he had taken me up at sea, and how generously he had treated me on all occasions, I took one hundred of the moidores, and called for a pen and ink to give him a receipt for them. Then I returned him the rest, and told him if ever I had possession of the plantation I would return the other to him also (as, indeed, I afterward did); and that, as to the bill of sale of his part of his son's ship, I would not take it by any means, but that if I wanted the money, I found he was honest enough to pay me; and if I did not, but came to receive what he gave me reason to expect, I would never have a penny more from him.

When this was past, the old man asked me if he should put me into the way of making my claim to my plantation. I told him I thought to go over to it myself. He said I might do so if I pleased, but that if I did not, there were ways enough to secure my right, and immediately to appropriate the profits to my use; and as there were ships in the river of Lisbon just ready to go away to Brazil, he made me enter my name in a public register, with his affidavit, affirming, upon oath, that I was alive, and that I was the same person who first took up the land for the planting of the said plantation.

This being formally attested by a notary, and a procuration affixed, he directed me to send it, with a letter of his writing, to a merchant of his acquaintance at the place, and then proposed my staying with him till an account came of the return.

Never was anything more honest than the proceedings upon this procuration, for in less than seven months, I received a large packet from the survivors of my trustees, the merchants, for whose account I went to sea.

Not to make a long story of this, I was now master, all of a sudden, of about five thousand pounds sterling in money, and had an estate, as I might well call it, in Brazil, of about a thousand pounds a year, as sure as an estate of lands in England; and, in a word, I was in a condition which I scarce knew how to understand, or how to compose myself for the enjoyment of it.

The first thing I did was to recompense my original benefactor, my good old captain, so I first returned the hundred moidores I had received of him. Then I sent for a notary and caused him to draw up a general release or discharge from the four hundred and seventy moidores, which he had acknowledged he owed me, in the fullest and firmest manner possible. After which I made a grant of one hundred moidores a year to him during his life, out of the proceeds of my estate, and fifty moidores a year to his son after him, for his life. And thus I repaid my fine old man.

Wishing now to return to England, I resolved to travel all the way by land, except from Calais to Dover. Making inquiries, I found three English merchants and two young Portuguese gentlemen, the last going to Paris only, so that there were six of us and five servants.

In this manner I set out from Lisbon.

As I have not troubled you with any of my sea journals, so I shall not trouble you now with any of my land journals, but some adventures that happened to us in this tedious and difficult journey I must not omit. When we came to the edge of Navarre, we were alarmed at several towns on the way with an account that so much snow had fallen on the French side of the mountains, that several wayfarers were obliged to come back to Pamplona after having attempted, at an extreme hazard, to go farther.

While I was considering this, there came in four French gentlemen, who having been stopped on the French side of the passes, as we were on the Spanish, had found a guide who, traversing the country near the head of Languédoc, had brought them over the mountains by such ways that they were not much inconvenienced with the snow; for where they met with snow in any quantity, they said it was frozen hard enough to bear them and their horses.

Accordingly, we set out from Pamplona, with our guide, on the 15th of November. When we approached the mountains, the hills and precipices looked dreadful, yet our guide made so many tours, such meanders, and led us by such winding ways, that we passed the height of the mountains without being much bothered with the snow; and, all of a sudden, he showed us the pleasant, fruitful provinces of Languédoc and Gascony, all green and flourishing, though, indeed, at a great distance, and we had some rough way to pass still.

We were a little uneasy, however, when we found it snowed one whole day and a night so fast that we could not travel, but he bid us be easy for we should soon be past it all. We found, indeed, that we began to descend every day, and to come more north than before; and so, depending upon our guide, we ventured further still.

One day we espied a bear coming out of the woods, and a vast, monstrous one it was, the biggest by far that ever I saw. We were all a little surprised when we saw him; but when Friday saw him, it was easy to see joy and courage in the fellow's countenance. "Oh – oh – oh!" says Friday, three times, pointing to him. "O, master! you give me leave, me shake hand with him, me make you good laugh."

So down he sits, and takes off his boots in a moment, and puts on a pair of pumps (as we call the flat shoes they wear, and which he had in his pocket), gives my other servant his horse, and with his gun, away he flew, swift as the north wind.

The bear was walking gently on, and offered no menace to anybody, till Friday, coming pretty near, takes a great stone and throws it at him, and hits him right on the head. As soon as the bear felt the blow, and saw him, he turns round and comes after him, taking long strides, and shuffling in a strange gait, such as would put a horse to a middling gallop; away runs Friday, and takes his course as if he ran toward us for help; so we all resolved to fire at once upon the bear, and deliver my man from possible death.

He cried out: "No shoot, no shoot. Stand still, and you get much laugh;" and as the nimble creature ran two feet for the bear's one, he turned on a sudden, on one side of us, and seeing a great oak tree fit for his purpose, he beckoned to us to follow; and doubling his pace, he gets nimbly up the tree, laying his gun down upon the ground at about five or six yards from the bottom of the tree. The bear soon came to the tree, and we followed at a distance.

The first thing he did was to stop at the gun and smell it, but let it lie, and up he scrambles into the tree, climbing like a cat, though so monstrous heavy. I was amazed at the folly, as I thought it, of my man, and could not for the life of me see anything to laugh at yet, till, seeing the bear get up the tree, we all rode nearer to him.

When we came to the tree, there was Friday out on the small end of a large branch, and the bear about halfway to him. As soon as the bear got out to that part where the limb of the tree was weaker, "Ha!" says he to us, "now you see me teach the bear dance." So he falls ajumping and shaking the bough, at which the bear began to totter, but stood still, and began to look behind him, to see how he should get back; then, indeed, we did laugh heartily. But Friday had not done with him by a great deal; for, seeing him stand still, he calls out to him again, as if he had supposed the bear could speak English: "What, you come no farther? Pray you come farther." So he stopped jumping and shaking the tree, and the bear, just as if he understood what he said, did come a little farther. Then he fell ajumping again, and the bear stopped again. Friday, seeing the bear cling fast to the bough, and that he would not be persuaded to come any farther: "Well, well," says Friday, "you no come farther, me go; you no come to me, me come to you"; and upon this, he goes out to the smaller end of the bough, where it would bend with his weight, and gently lets himself down with it, sliding down the bough, till he came near enough to jump down on his feet, and away he runs to his gun, takes it up, and stands still.

When the bear saw his enemy gone, he comes back from the bough where he stood, mighty cautiously, looking behind him at every step, and coming backward till he got into the body of the tree. Then, with his back end foremost, he came down the tree, grasping it with his claws, and moving one foot at a time, very leisurely. At this juncture, and just before he could set his hindfoot on the ground, Friday stepped up close to him, clapped the muzzle of the piece into his ear, and shot him dead. Then the rogue turned round, to see if we did not laugh; and when he saw we were pleased, by our looks, he falls laughing himself, very loud. "So we kill bear in my country," says Friday.

"So how do you kill them?" asks I, "when you have no guns."

"No," says he, "no gun, but shoot him with much long arrow."

These things, and the approach of night, called us off, or else, as Friday would have had us, we should certainly have taken the skin of this monstrous creature off, which was worth saving; but we had near three leagues to go, and our guide hastened us, so we left him, and went forward on our journey.

We had not gone halfway over the plain when we began to hear the wolves howl in a frightful manner in the woods on our left.

The night was coming on, and the light began to be dusky, which made it worse on our side; but the noise increasing, we would easily perceive that it was the howling and yelling of these hellish creatures; and on a sudden we perceived two or three troops of wolves, one on our left, one behind us, and one in our front, so that we seemed surrounded by them. However, as they did not fall upon us, we kept our

I saw a man with his hands and feet tied (page 129)

The fresh water revived him wonderfully (page 135)

way forward, as fast as we could make our horses go, which, the way being very rough, was only a good hard trot. In this manner we came in view of the entrance of the woods, through which we were to pass, at the farther side of the plain.

We were greatly surprised when, coming nearer the pass, we saw a number of wolves standing just at the entrance. It happened very much to our advantage, that at the entrance into the woods, but a little way from it, there lay some large timber trees which had been cut down the summer before, and I suppose lay there for haulage. I drew my little troop in among those trees, and placing ourselves in a line behind one long tree, I advised them all to alight, and keeping that tree before us for protection, to stand in a triangle or three fronts enclosing our horses in the middle.

We did so, and it was well we did, for never was there a more furious charge than the creatures made upon in this place. They came on with a growling kind of noise, and mounted the piece of timber, which, I said, was our protection, as if they were only rushing upon their prey; and this fury of theirs, it seems, was principally occasioned by their seeing our horses behind us. I ordered our men to fire as before, every other man, and they took their aim so sure that they killed several of the wolves at the first volley; but it was necessary to keep a constant firing, for they came on like devils, those behind pushing on those before.

I was not keen to spend our shot too hastily, so I called a servant, and giving him a horn of powder, I bade him lay a trail all along the piece of timber, and do so in a large trail. He did so, and had but just time to get away when the wolves came up to it, and some got upon it, when I, snapping an uncharged pistol close to the powder, set it on fire; those that were upon the timber were scorched with it, and six or seven of them fell or rather jumped in among us, with the force and fright of the fire. We dispatched these in an instant, and the rest were so frightened with the light, which the night, for it was now very near dark, made more terrible, that they all fled and left us.

In about an hour more we came to the town where we were to lodge.

The next morning our guide was so ill that he could go no farther, so we were obliged to take a new guide here and go to Toulouse, where we found a warm climate, a pleasant country, and no snow, no wolves, nor anything like them.

I have nothing uncommon to take notice of in my passage through France, nothing but what others have given an account of, with much more advantage than I can. I journeyed from Toulouse to Paris, and without any prolonged stay, came to Calais, and then from there safe to Dover on the 14th of January, after a severe cold season to travel in.

I had, in a short time, all my new discovered estate safe about me, the bills of exchange which I brought with me having been paid very expeditiously.

My principal guide and private advisor was my good ancient widow, who, in gratitude for the money I had sent her, thought no pains too much, nor care too great, for me; and I trusted her so entirely with everything that I was perfectly easy to the security of my effects; and, indeed, I was very happy from the beginning, and now to the end, in the unspotted integrity of this good gentlewoman.

I now resolved to dispose of my plantation in Brazil, if I could find means. For this purpose, I wrote to my old friend at Lisbon, who, after offering it to the two merchants, the survivors of my trustees, who lived in Brazil, they accepted the offer, and remitted thirty-three thousand pieces of eight to a correspondent of theirs at Lisbon to pay for it. Having signed the instrument of sale, and sent it to my old friend, he remitted me bills of exchange for thirty-two thousand eight hundred pieces of eight for the estate, reserving the payment of a hundred moidores a year to himself during his life and fifty moidores afterward to his son for life, which I had promised them.

Though I had sold my estate in Brazil, yet I could not keep the country out of my head, nor could I resist the strong inclination I had to see my island. At times my imagination was worked up to such a height that I supposed myself at my old castle behind the trees, saw my old Spaniard, Friday's father, and the reprobate sailors I had left upon the island. I even fancied I talked with them, though I was wide awake!

One time, in my sleep, I had the villainy of the three pirate sailors so lively related to me by the first Spaniard and Friday's father that it was surprising. My true friend, the widow, earnestly dissuaded me from it, and so far prevailed with me, that for almost seven years, she prevented my going away, during which time I took my two nephews, the children of one my brothers, into my care. The eldest, having something of his own, I bred up as a gentleman and gave him a settlement of some addition to his estate, after my decease. The other I put out as captain of a ship, and after five years, finding him a sensible, bold, enterprising young fellow, I put him into a good ship, and sent him to sea; and this young fellow afterward drew me in, old as I was, to further adventures myself.

In the meantime, I settled myself here. First of all, I married, and that not either to my disadvantage or dissatisfaction, and had three children, two sons and one daughter. But when my wife died, and my nephew came home with good success from a voyage to Spain, my inclination to go abroad increased. Eventually my nephew proposed I go in his ship as a private trader to the East Indies. This was in the year 1694.

CHAPTER TWELVE
THE ISLAND REVISITED

One day my nephew came to me and told me that some merchants of his acquaintance had been proposing to him to voyage to the East Indies and to China, as private traders. "And now, uncle," says he, "if you will go to sea with me, I will engage to land you upon your old habitation in the island, for we are to touch at Brazil."

The scheme hit so exactly with my feelings that I told him I would go with him, but no farther than my island. Not wishing to be left stranded there, and it being impossible for the ship to return to me, I had decided that we would carry a framed sloop on board the ship, which being taken in pieces and shipped as cargo on the ship, might, by the help of some carpenters whom we agreed to carry with us, be set up again in the island and finished, fit to go to sea, in a few days.

My nephew was ready to sail about the beginning of January, 1694-5, and I, with my man Friday, went on board in the Downs on the 8th, having, besides that sloop which I mentioned before, a very extensive cargo of all kinds of necessary things for my colony, which, if I did not find in good condition, I resolved to leave so.

I shall trouble nobody with the incidents of our voyage except to mention a very distant view of that most lamentable sight, a large ship on fire in the middle of the sea; but to shorten my story, for the sake of what is to follow, I shall merely observe that I came to my old habitation, the island, on the 10th of April, 1695.

As we went on shore upon the tide of flood near high water, we rowed directly into the creek, and the first man that I fixed my eye upon was the Spaniard whose life I had saved. I ordered that nobody go on shore but myself, but there was no keeping Friday in the boat, for the affectionate creature had spied his father at a distance, a good way off, where indeed I could see nothing of him, and if they had not let him go ashore, he would have jumped into the sea. He was no sooner on shore but he flew away to his father, like an arrow out of a bow. It would have made any man shed tears, in spite of the firmest resolution, to have seen the first transports of this poor fellow's joy when he came to his father: how he embraced him, kissed him, stroked his face, took him up in his arms, and then walked up and down the shore with his father for hours, always leading him by the hand as if he were a child.

It would be needless to take notice of all the ceremonies and civilities that the Spaniards greeted me with. The first Spaniard, who, as I said, I knew very well, was he whose life I had saved. While I was greeting him, there arrived eleven at his party. The story my old friend told me of what had happened on the island since my departure was so interesting that I must set it down, more or less as it was told to me.

It took my old friend but three weeks to find his countrymen and return to the island, but in that time, unluckily for them, I had the occasion offered for my escape, as I mentioned in my other part, and to get off the island, leaving three of the most impudent, hardened, ungoverned, disagreeable villains behind me that any person would be sorry to meet, to the poor Spaniards' great grief and disappointment, you may be sure.

At first the rogues behaved fairly well, giving the Spaniards my long list of directions, nor did they refuse to accommodate the newcomers in other ways, for they agreed very well for some time. They gave them an equal admission into the house, or cave, and they began to live very sociably; and the head

Spaniard, who had seen pretty much of my methods, together with Friday's father, managed all their affairs. As for the Englishmen, they did nothing but ramble about the island, shoot parrots, and catch tortoises, and when they came home at night, the Spaniards provided their suppers for them. But differences soon broke out which at last resulted in open war.

Before I come to the particulars of this part, I must correct a defect in my former narrative. This was, I forgot to set down, among the rest, that just as we were weighing the anchor to set sail, a second mutiny was threatened and the captain put two of the most refractory fellows ashore. These two men made their number five, but the other three villains were so much more wicked than they, that after they had been two or three days together, they turned the two newcomers out of doors to shift for themselves, and would have nothing to do with them; not could they, for a good while, be persuaded to give them any food. As for the Spaniards, they had not yet come.

So the two poor fellows lived by themselves, and pitched their tents on the north shore of the island.

Here they built two huts, one to lodge in and the other to lay up their magazines and stores in. The Spaniards when they arrived, having given them some corn for seed, and especially some of the peas which I had left them, they dug, planted and enclosed, after the pattern I had set for them all, and began to live pretty well. Their first crop of corn was harvested, and though it was but a little bit of land which they dug up first, having had but a little time, yet it was enough to relieve them and provide them with bread and other eatables.

They were going on in this little thriving way when the three unnatural rogues began to bully them, and told them the island was theirs, that the governor, meaning me, had given them the possession of it, and that they could not build houses upon their ground unless they would pay rent for them. This the two men resisted stoutly and in the fight that arose between them, the two, being able to come at their weapons, prevailed; but afterwards they paid dearly for their success, for the villains persecuted them outrageously.

But not to crowd this part with an account of the lesser part of their foul play, such as treading down their corn; shooting three young kids and a goat, which the poor men had tamed and bred for their store; and, in a word, plaguing them night and day in this manner, it forced the two men to such a desperation that they resolved to fight them all three.

In order to do this, they went early one morning to the castle, as they called it (that was, my old dwelling), and asked the Spaniards to stand by to see fair play done.

It happened that the day before, the Spaniards themselves had been subjected to the same demand for rent. They only smiled at that, and made no other answer.

Upon this the three rogues went trooping away, every man with a gun, a pistol, and a sword, and muttered some insolent things among themselves of what they would do to the Spaniards when opportunity offered.

Whither they went, or how they bestowed their time that evening, the Spaniards said they did not know; but it seems they wandered around the country part of the night and then, lying down in the place which I used to call my bower, they were weary and overslept themselves. The case was this: they had resolved to stay till midnight, and so take the two poor men when they were asleep, and, as they acknowledged afterward, intended to set fire to their huts while they were in them, and either let them burn alive or murder them as they came out to safety.

When they came there and found the men gone, they fell to work with the poor men's habitation, and, in a word, sacked and plundered everything as completely as a horde of barbarians would have done.

When the three came back like furious creatures, flushed with the rage which the work they had been about had put them into, they came up to the Spaniards and told them what they had done by way of bravado, threatening to do the like to them. In the ensuing scuffle, the three ruffians were disarmed. The Spaniards said that if the three would live peaceably, they would receive help as before and be allowed to mix freely with the others, but no arms would be allowed them while they persisted in their present attitude of threatening mischief and servitude, not to their two countrymen only, but to everyone on the island. The rogues were no longer capable of listening to reason, just as they could not act with reason, but being refused their arms, they went away, raging and swearing like furies.

In about five days' time the three vagrants, tired with wandering, and almost starved with hunger, having chiefly lived on turtle's eggs all that while, came back to the grove. Upon finding my Spaniard, who, as I have said, was the governor, and two more with him walking by the side of the creek, they came up in a very submissive, humble manner, and begged to be received again into the family. The Spaniards obliged the three to go and rebuild their fellows' two huts, one to be of the same size, and the other of larger dimensions than they were before, and, in a word, to restore everything in the state they found it, as near as they could.

Well, they submitted to all this, and as they had plenty of provisions given them all the while, they grew very orderly, and the whole society began to live pleasantly and agreeably together once more.

It happened one night that the Spanish governor, as I call him, that is to say, the Spaniard whose life I had saved and who was now the captain or leader of the rest, being unable to sleep, arose and went out of doors, accompanied by another Spaniard whom the noise he made had awakened. They were going round through the grove, unconcerned and unwary, when they were surprised by seeing a light like a fire a very little distance from them, and hearing the voices of Indians, not one or two, but of a great number.

We need not doubt but that the governor and the man with him, surprised by this sight, ran back immediately and raised their fellows, giving them an account of the immediate danger they were all in.

While it was still dark, they sent the old Indian,

Friday's father, out as a spy to learn, if possible, something concerning the cannibals: what they had come for, what they intended to do, and the like. After he had been gone an hour or two, he brought word that he had been among them undiscovered; that he found they were two parties, each of different nations, who had war with one another, and had a great battle in their own country; and that both sides having had several prisoners taken in the fight, they had, by mere chance, all landed on the same island, for the purpose of devouring their prisoners and making merry, but their coming so by chance to the same place had spoiled all their mirth; that they were in a great rage at one another, and were so near battle that he believed they would fight again as soon as daylight began to appear. And thus it turned out.

The battle was very fierce and lasted two hours before they could guess which party would be beaten; but then that party which was nearest our people's habitation began to fly. Three, crossing the creek, ran directly into the grove, not in the least knowing whither they went, but running as into a thick wood for shelter. These were taken prisoners without much difficulty by the others.

The residue of the conquered people fled to their canoes, and got off to sea. The victors made no pursuit but, drawing themselves into a body together, gave two screaming shouts, which the white men supposed was by way of triumph, and so the fight ended. And the same day, about three o'clock in the afternoon, they also marched to their canoes and embarked. And thus the Spaniards had their island to themselves again; their fright was over and they saw no cannibals for several years afterward.

This deliverance tamed our Englishmen for a long time. They all lived two years after this in perfect isolation and had no more visits from the cannibals. They had indeed an alarm given to them one morning which put them into great consternation, for some of the Spaniards being out early one morning on the west side, or rather end, of that island (which was that end where I never went, for fear of being discovered), they were surprised by seeing about twenty canoes of Indians just coming on shore. They made their way home as quickly as they could and, giving the alarm to their comrades, they kept close to home all that day and the next, going out only at night to make their observation; but they had the good luck to be mistaken about where the Indians were going, for they did not land on the island that time, but pursued some other plan.

And now they had another problem with the three

mutineers, and learned from one of the two honest Englishmen how Will Atkins, one of the three, had proposed to have all the five Englishmen join together and murder all the Spaniards when they were sleeping.

After a long debate, it was agreed, first, that they should be disarmed and not permitted to have either gun, powder, shot, sword, or any weapon, and should be turned out of the society and left to live where they would and how they would, by themselves; also that none of the rest, either Spaniards or English, would converse with them, work with them, or have anything to do with them, that they should not be allowed to come within a certain distance of the place where the rest lived.

The three ruffians pitched their tents and marked themselves out a habitation and plantation in a very convenient place, indeed, on the remotest part of the island.

Here they built themselves two handsome huts, and arranged them in a manner like my first habitation, but close under the side of a hill, having some trees growing already on three sides of it, so that by planting others, it would be very easily covered from sight, unless particularly searched for. They desired some dried goatskins for beds and

I could see a ship lying at anchor (page 139)

We surprised the two men before they were aware (page 155)

In the boat were the things promised to the men (page 167)

So he falls ajumping and shaking the bough (page 178)

coverings, which were given them; and upon giving their word that they would not disturb the rest, or injure any of their plantations, the Spaniards gave them hatchets and what other tools they could spare, some peas, barley, and rice, for sowing, and, in a word, anything they wanted except for arms and ammunition.

About three quarters of a year after this separation, a whim took these three that they would make a voyage to the continent, from whence the Indians came, and would try if they could to seize some prisoners among the natives there and bring them home in order to make them do the hardest part of the work.

The Spaniards told them, with great kindness, that if they were resolved to go, they should not go like naked men, and be in no position to defend themselves: and that, though firearms could be ill spared, yet the adventurers should have two muskets, a pistol, and a cutlass, and each man a hatchet. In a word, the three accepted the offer; and having baked enough bread to last them a month, and as much goat's flesh as they could eat while it was sweet, and a great basket of dried grapes, a pot of fresh water, and a young kid alive, they boldly set out in the canoe for a voyage over the sea, where it was at least forty miles broad. After two-and-twenty days' absence they returned.

They gave the Spaniards a full account of their voyage in a few words: they reached the land in two days or something less, but finding the people alarmed at their coming, and prepared with bows and arrows to fight them, they dared not go on shore, but sailed on to the northward six or seven hours, till they came to a great opening by which they perceived that the land they saw from our island was not the main, but an island. Upon entering that opening of the sea, they saw another island on the right hand, north, and several more west; and having resolved to land somewhere, they put over to one of the islands which lay west, and went boldly on shore. There they found the people very courteous and friendly to them, so they stayed there four days.

They were told by the people that their great king had two hundred prisoners whom he had taken in his war, and they were feeding them to make them fat for the next feast. The Englishmen seemed mightly desirous of seeing those prisoners; but the others, thinking them cannibals too, brought down five women and three men and gave them to the Englishmen to carry with them on their voyage, just as we would bring so many cows and oxen down to a seaport town to supply a ship before a long voyage.

The Englishmen were obliged to come away as soon as they had them, or else the givers would certainly have expected their visitors to go to work and kill two or three of the captives the next morning, and perhaps to invite the donors to a great feast. When the three wanderers had given this journal of their voyage, the whole colony went down to the place of the prisoners' confinement to see them. When they came into the hut, there they sat, all of them bound.

First, there were three men, lusty, comely fellows, well-shaped with straight and fair limbs, about thirty to thirty-five years of age; and five women of whom two might be from thirty to forty, two more not above four- or five-and-twenty and the fifth, a tall, comely maiden, about sixteen or seventeen. The women were good-tempered, agreeable persons, both in shape and features, only tawny of skin; of a very modest conduct, especially when they came afterward to be clothed and dressed, though that dress was very indifferent, it must be confessed.

The five Englishmen each took a wife, and so they set up a new style of living: for the Spaniards and Friday's father lived in my old habitation, which they had enlarged greatly inside. The three servants, who were taken in the late battle of the cannibals, lived with them, and these carried on the main part of the colony, supplied all the rest with food, and assisted them in anything as they could, or as they found necessity required. The three wicked ones had pitched farthest off and the two honest ones nearer, but both on the north shore of the island, so that they continued separated as before.

And this is how my island was peopled in three places, and, as I might say, made the start of three towns.

CHAPTER THIRTEEN
THE SPANIARD'S STORY

I now come to a scene different from all that had happened before, either to them or to me. The start of the story was this: early one morning, there came on shore five or six canoes of Indians or cannibals, call them which you please, and there is no doubt they came upon the old errand of feeding upon their slaves. All the colony had to do was to lie concealed, and this they did with just as much success as before.

After the canoes with the natives had gone off, the Spaniards stirred outside again, and some of them had the curiosity to go to the place where the Indians had been to see what they had been doing. Here, to their great surprise, they found three of them left behind, lying fast asleep upon the ground.

The poor fellows were exceedingly frightened when they were seized upon and bound. Afterward they were carried to the habitation of the two Englishmen.

Here they were set to work, though there was not

much for them to do, and whether it was by negligence in guarding them, or, it was thought, the fellows could not get used to the life I know not, but one of them ran away, and taking to the woods, was never heard of any more.

There was good reason to believe he got home again soon after in some other boats or canoes of cannibals who came on shore three or four weeks afterward, and who, carrying on their revels as usual, went off in two days' time. This Indian had never been told, and it was very lucky he had not, how many there were on the island or where they lived; nor had he ever seen or heard the fire of any of their guns, much less had they shown him any of the other hidden places, such as the cave in the valley, or new retreats, which the two Englishmen had made, and the like.

The first sign they had that this fellow had given word of them was that, about two months after this, six canoes of cannibals with about seven, eight, or ten men in a canoe, came rowing along the north side of the island, where they never used to come before. There they landed about an hour after sunrise at a convenient place, about a mile from the habitation of the two Englishmen, where this escaped man had been kept. The two men had the good fortune to spot them about a league off at sea, so that it was about an hour before they landed, and as they landed about a mile from the huts, it was some time before they could attack.

Now, having great reason to believe that they had been betrayed, the first thing the two Englishmen did was to bind the two slaves who were left, and cause two of the three men who were brought with the women (who it seems proved very faithful to their masters) to lead them, with their two wives, and whatever they could carry away with them, to their places in the woods, which I have spoken of above, and there to bind the two fellows hand and foot, till they learned more.

When the two, poor, frightened men had secured their wives and goods, they sent the other slave they had of the three who came with the women, and who was at the place by accident, away to the Spaniards with all speed, to warn them and ask for speedy help; and, in the meantime, they took their arms and what ammunition they had, and retreated toward the place in the woods where their wives were sent, keeping at a distance at which they might see, if possible, which way the cannibals went.

They had not gone far before, from a rising ground, they could see the little army of their enemies come on directly to their habitation, and, in a minute more, could see all their huts and household stuff going up in flames, to their great grief and mortification; for they suffered a very great loss, indeed, irretrievable, at least for some time.

They then retreated into a very overgrown part of the woods where an old tree trunk stood, which was hollow and vastly large, and in this tree they concealed themselves carefully, resolving to see there what might happen. They had not been there long before two of the cannibals appeared, running directly their way, and a little way farther they espied three more coming after them, and five more beyond them, all coming the same way, besides which, they saw seven or eight more at a distance running another way; for, in a word, they ran every way, like sportsmen beating for their game.

The two Englishmen allowed the first two to pass and waited until the three, followed by the five, were almost upon them.

While they were thus waiting, and the cannibals came on, they plainly saw that one of the three was the runaway savage who had escaped from them. They both knew him positively and resolved that, if possible, he should not escape, though they both had to fire. So the other stood ready with his gun, that if he did not drop at the first shot, he should be sure to receive a second. But the first was too good a marksman to miss his aim and, as the cannibals kept near one another, a little behind in a line, he fired, and hit two of them directly: the foremost was killed outright, being shot in the head; the second, who was the runaway slave, was shot through the body, and fell, but was not quite dead; and the third had a little scratch in the shoulder, perhaps by the same ball that went through the body of the second, and being dreadfully frightened, though not so much hurt, sat down upon the ground, screaming and yelling in a hideous manner.

The five that were behind, more frightened by the noise than alarmed by the danger, came to the place where their companions lay in a miserable condition; and here the poor, ignorant creatures, not understanding that they were within reach of the same mischief, stood all of a huddle over the wounded man, talking, and, as may be supposed, inquiring of him how he came to be hurt.

Our two men, the first having loaded his gun again, shot together and killed, or very much wounded, four of them. The fifth, frightened almost to death, though not hurt, fell with the rest, so that our men, seeing them all fall together, thought that they had killed all of them with their shot.

The two Englishmen came boldly out of the tree, killed the runaway slave with the stocks of their muskets, put a wounded man out of his pain and bound the man who was not hurt at all to the foot of a tree. Their first concern now was to ascertain if the Indians had discovered the hiding place of the women, and to calm their fears if they had been frightened by the fight.

When they came there, they found the Indians had been in the woods very near that place, but had not found it: for it was inaccessible behind the trees standing so thick, unless those seeking it had been directed by those that knew it, which these did not. They found, therefore, everything was safe, but the women were in a terrible fright. While they were here, they had the comfort to have seven of the Spaniards come to their assistance. The other ten, with their servants, and old Friday, I mean Friday's father, had gone together to defend their bower and the corn and cattle that was kept there, in case the cannibals should have wandered over to that side of the country; but they had not gone so far.

When the Spaniards came, the two Englishmen were so encouraged that they resolved, though with all possible caution, to go forward, toward their ruined plantation; but a little before they came thither, coming in sight of the seashore, they plainly saw the Indians embarking in their canoes in order to be gone. The colonists seemed sorry, at first, that there was no way to reach their invaders to give them a parting blow; but, on the whole, they were very well satisfied to be rid of them.

It was five or six months after this before they heard any more of the Indians, in which time our men were in hopes they had given up the idea of another invasion. Then, all of a sudden, the little island was invaded with a most formidable fleet of no less than eight-and-twenty canoes packed full of cannibals, armed with bows and arrows, great clubs, wooden swords, and other instruments of war; and they brought such numbers with them that, in short, it put all our people into the utmost consternation.

As they came on shore in the evening, and at the easternmost side of the island, our men had the night to consult and consider what to do. They knew that their being entirely concealed had been their only safety before, and would be much more so now that the number of their enemies was so great, so they therefore resolved, first of all, to take down the huts which, by the combined efforts of all, including the three rascals, had been rebuilt for the two Englishmen, and drive away their goats to the old cave, for they supposed the cannibals would go directly thither as soon as it was day, to play the old game over again, though they had not now landed within two leagues of it.

The next morning, early, the colonists posted themselves with all their force at the plantation of the two men, to wait for the enemy.

The Indians, to the number of two hundred and fifty as near as our men could judge, came forward like lions until Will Atkins, who, with six men, was planted behind a thicket as an advance guard, poured two volleys into them from behind. Had he and his men retreated the moment they had fired, as they were ordered to do, the savages would have been completely routed, for the terror that was among them came principally from their idea that they were killed by the gods with thunder and lightning, but could see nobody that hurt them.

But Will Atkins, staying to load again, was discovered. Some of the Indians who were at a distance spying on them, came upon them from behind, and though Atkins and his men fired at them two or three times, and killed about twenty while retreating as fast as they could, they wounded Atkins and killed one of his fellow Englishmen, as they did one Spaniard and one of the Indian slaves who came with the women. The Spaniards, after firing three volleys upon them, retreated also, for their number was so small. Further, the Indians were so desperate, that though about fifty of them were killed and more than that number wounded, yet they came on in the teeth of our men, fearless of danger, and shot their arrows like a cloud. It was also observed that their wounded men, who were not quite disabled, seemed to go mad from their wounds and fought even more furiously.

When our men retreated, the enemy did not seem to pursue them, but drew themselves up in a ring, which is, it seems, their custom, and shouted twice, in token of their victory. After this they had the mortification to see several of their wounded men fall, dying because of their loss of blood.

The Spaniards now decided to fight no more until morning, when the other wounded Indians would be dead or faint from loss of blood; but a clear moonlight night ensuing, and the enemy crowding in great disorder about their dead and wounded, the Spaniards surrounded them. They poured volleys in upon them from all sides, and winning a complete victory, then cut them off from their canoes, which, upon the advice of Will Atkins, were then utterly destroyed so they could not be used for escape.

In these two fights, our men killed or mortally wounded about one hundred and eighty of the enemy. The rest, being frightened out of their wits, scoured through the woods and over the hills with all the speed that fear and nimble feet could help them to. The best thing was that they had no weapons, for though they had bows, they had no arrows left, nor any materials to make any; nor had they any cutting tool or weapon among them.

The extremity and distress they were reduced to was great and indeed deplorable, and many were afterward found dead in the woods, unhurt, but starved to death.

When our men found this, it made their hearts relent, and pity moved them, especially the Spanish governor who was the most gentleman-like, generous-minded man that I ever met in my life; and he proposed to send them an offer through a prisoner who had been taken.

This offer, which had been communicated to the captive by old Friday, was to give the Indians part of the island to live in, provided they would give assurances that they would keep in their own bounds and not come beyond it to injure or prejudice others. In turn, they would have corn given them to plant and grow for their bread, and some food given them for their present subsistence.

The poor wretches, thoroughly humbled, and reduced in number to about thirty-seven, agreed to the proposal on the first offer. They were confined to a neck of land surrounded by high rocks behind and lying straight toward the sea before them, on the southeast corner of the island. They had land enough, about a mile and a half broad and three or four miles in length, and it was very good and fruitful.

Our men taught them to make wooden spades, such as I made for myself, and gave them twelve hatchets and three or four knives; and there they lived, the most innocent creatures that ever were heard of.

After this, the colony enjoyed a perfect peace with respect to the Indians, as they were when I came to revisit them, which was about two years later.

Having thus given a view of the state of things as I found them, I must relate the deeds of what I did for these people, and the condition in which I left them. It was their opinion, and mine too, that they would be troubled no more with the Indians or, if they were, they would be able to cut them off if they were twice as many as before, so they had no concern about that any longer.

Then I entered into a serious discourse with the Spaniard, whom I call governor, about their stay in the island; for as I had not come to carry any of them off, it would not be just to carry off some and leave others, who, perhaps, would be unwilling to stay if their strength was diminished.

On the other hand, I told them I came to establish them there, not to remove them, and then I let them know that I had brought with me relief of sundry kinds for them; that I had been at great pains to supply them with all things necessary for their convenience as well as their safety; and that, as well, I had such and such particular persons with me to increase and improve their number, these being craftsmen of various kinds, of journeyman skills having been apprenticed and trained up, to assist them in those things in which they were at present in want.

They were all together when I talked thus to them, and before I delivered to them the stores I had brought, I asked them one by one, if they had entirely given over and buried the first animosities that had been among them, and if they would shake hands with one another and engage in a strict friendship and union of interest, so that there might be no more misunderstandings and jealousies.

A large ship on fire in the middle of the sea (page 189)

Friday led him by the hand as if he were a child
(page 190)

Most frank and open declarations were made on both sides.

Will Atkins had behaved himself so bravely in the great fight with the enemy that the Spaniards had forgiven his past actions and thought he merited as much to be trusted with arms and supplied with necessities as any of them, and they had testified their satisfaction in him by naming him next in command to the governor himself. As they now had entire confidence in him, and all his countrymen, so they acknowledged they had merited that confidence by all the methods that honest men could merit to be valued and trusted; and they most heartily embraced the occasion of giving me this assurance, that they would never have any interest separate from one another. Will Atkins proved no less cordial.

Upon this we made an appointment to dine all together the next day, and, indeed, we had a splendid feast.

After this feast, at which we were very innocently merry, I brought out my cargo of goods: wherein that there might be no dispute about dividing, I showed them that there was enough for them all, desiring that they might all take an equal quantity of goods that were for making clothes, that is to say, equal when actually made up. I cannot express what pleasure and what satisfaction sat upon the countenances of all these poor people when they saw the care I had taken for them, and how well I had furnished them. They told me I was a father to them, and that having such a friend as I was, though far away, would make them forget that they were left in a desolate place; and they all voluntarily undertook that they would not leave the place without my consent for it.

Then I presented to them the people I had brought with me, particularly the tailor, the smith, and the two carpenters, all of them most necessary people, but, above all, my general artisan, who was more useful to them than anyone else they could name.

Then I brought them out all my store of tools and gave every man a digging spade, a shovel, and a rake, for we had no harrows or ploughs; and to every separate place a pickaxe, a crowbar, a broad axe, and a saw; always remembering that, as often as any were broken or worn out, they should be supplied without grudging out of the general stores that I left behind. Nails, staples, hinges, hammers, chisels, knives, scissors, and all sorts of ironwork was there to last a long time, for no man would take more than he needed, and he must be a fool who would waste or spoil them on any account whatever. For the use of the smith, I left two tons of unwrought iron as a basic supply.

The magazine of powder and arms which I brought them was such, even to profusion, that they could not but rejoice at it, for now they could march as I used to do, with a musket upon each shoulder, if there was occasion; and would be able to fight a thousand of any enemy if they had but some little advantages of situation, which also they could not miss, if they had occasion.

And now the other two Englishmen changed their abode to a more fertile place, and so the island was divided into three colonies, and no more. The Spaniards, with old Friday and the first servants lived at my old habitation under the hill, which was, in a word, the capital city. They had so enlarged and extended their works here, under, as well as on, the outside of the hill, that they lived perfectly concealed, yet not confined at all.

The other colony was that of Will Atkins, where there were four families of Englishmen, I mean those I had left there, with their wives and children; three Indians who were slaves; the widow and the children of the Englishman that was killed, to whom the others were quick and generous in giving a full share of all their produce.

There were also the two carpenters and the tailor, whom I had brought with me for them; also the smith, who was a very necessary man to them, especially as a gunsmith, to take care of their arms; and my other man, whom I called Jack-of-all-Trades, who was in himself as good almost as twenty men, for he was not only a very ingenious fellow, but also a very merry character.

Having now done what I came to do, I left them all in good circumstances and in a flourishing condition, and went on board my ship again on the 6th of May, having been about twenty-five days among them; and as they were all resolved to stay upon the island till I came to remove them, I promised to send them further relief from Brazil, if I could possibly find an opportunity; and, particularly, I promised to send them some cattle, such as sheep, hogs, and cows. As to the two cows and calves which I had brought from England, we had been obliged, by the length of our voyage, to kill them at sea, for lack of hay to feed them.

CHAPTER FOURTEEN
PERIL BY SEA

The next day, giving them a salute of five guns at parting, we set sail, and arrived at the Bay of All Saints in Brazil in about twenty-two days, meeting nothing remarkable in our passage but this. On the third day, toward evening, the sea smooth, and the ship lying becalmed, we saw about a hundred canoes coming toward us. They came on apace, so I gave orders to come to an anchor and furl all our sails. As for the Indians, I told our men they had nothing to fear but fire, and therefore they should get their boats out and fasten them, one close by the head, and the other by the stern, and man them both well, and wait to see what would happen. This I did so that the men in the boats might be ready with sheets and buckets to put out any fire these cannibals would attempt to fix to the outside of the ship.

In this way we lay in wait for them, and in a little while they caught up with us.

When they came nearer to us, they seemed to be

struck with wonder and astonishment, as at a sight which doubtless they had never seen before; nor could they, at first, as we afterward understood, know what to make of us. They came boldly up, however, very near to us, and seemed to be trying to row round us; but we called to our men in the boats not to let them come too near them. This very order brought us to an engagement with them, without our planning it: for five or six of the large canoes came so near the longboat that our men beckoned with their hands to keep them back, which they understood very well, and went back, but at their retreat, about fifty arrows came on board us from those boats, and one of our men in the longboat was very badly wounded. However, I called to our men not to fire back in any way. Then we handed down some wooden planks into the boat, and the carpenter quickly built a kind of fence, like waste boards, to cover them from the arrows of the savages, if they should start to shoot again.

About half an hour afterward, the Indians all came up in a body astern of us, and so near that we could easily discern what they were, though we could not tell their plan; and I easily found they were some of my old friends, the same sort of cannibals that I had been used to engage with; and in a short time more they rowed a little farther out to sea, till they came so near that they could hear us speak. Upon this I ordered all my men to keep close, lest they should shoot any more arrows, and made all our guns ready; but being so near as to be within hearing, I made Friday go out upon the deck and call out aloud to them in their language, to find out what they meant to do, which accordingly he did.

Immediately afterward, Friday cried out they were going to shoot, and, unhappily for him, poor fellow, they let fly about three hundred of their arrows, and, to my inexpressible grief killed poor Friday, no other man being in their sight. The poor fellow was shot with only three of their arrows, and about three more fell very near him, such poor marksmen were they!

I was so enraged at the loss of my trusty servant and companion that I immediately ordered five guns to be loaded with small shot, and four with great, and gave them such a broadside as they had never heard in their lives before, to be sure. They were not more than half a cable length off when we fired.

I can neither tell how many we killed nor how many we wounded with this broadside, but surely such a fright and hurry never was seen among such a multitude. There were thirteen or fourteen of their canoes split and overset in all, and the men all set aswimming. The rest, frightened out of their wits, scoured away as fast as they could, taking but little care to save those whose boats were split or spoiled with our shot. So I suppose that many of them were lost.

We were now under sail again, but I was the most disconsolate creature alive for grief over my beloved man Friday.

And now as I name the poor fellow once more, I must take my last leave of him. Poor honest Friday! We buried him with all the decency and solemnity possible by putting him into a coffin and throwing him into the sea; and I caused them to fire eleven guns for him. And so ended the life of the most grateful, faithful, honest, and most affectionate servant that ever a man had.

We now went away with a fair wind for Brazil, and in about twelve days' time we made land in the latitude of five degrees south of the line, being the northeasternmost land on all that part of America. We kept on south by east in sight of the shore four days, when we made Cape St. Augustine, and in three days came to an anchor off the bay of All Saints, the old place of my deliverance, from whence came both my good and evil fate.

From Brazil we sailed directly over the Atlantic

Ocean to the Cape of Good Hope and had a tolerably good voyage, our course generally southeast. Now and then we met a storm and some contrary winds, but my disasters at sea were at an end. My future problems and bad times were to befall me on shore.

We stayed at the Cape no longer than was needful to take in fresh water, and soon were on our way for the coast of Coromandel.

We touched first at the island of Madagascar, where we fared very well for a time. It happened, however, that one evening when we went on shore, one of our fellows, feeling himself insulted by a young native, struck him. This led to a free fight in which one of our sailors was killed by a lance that was thrown at him. Being outnumbered, our men were forced to retreat to the ship, whence they fired a broadside, loaded with pieces of iron and steel, small bullets and such stuff besides the great shot, which made a terrible havoc upon the natives. Nor did this revenge satisfy our crew, but they must go ashore at midnight and burn the village, killing both men and women.

I was very angry with my nephew, the captain, and indeed with all the men, but with him in particular, as prompting rather than cooling the rage of his crew in so cruel and bloody an enterprise. The next day we set sail. I always, after that time, told our men that God would blast the voyage, for I looked upon the blood they had shed that night to be murder in them.

We were now bound for the Gulf of Persia, and from thence to the coast of Coromandel, only to touch at Surat.

But my frequent preaching to them on the subject of their cruelties in Madagascar had worse consequences than I expected, for the boatswain, who had been at the head of the midnight raid, came up boldly to me one time and told me, that unless I would stop my preaching about it, and also not concern myself any further with him or any of his affairs, he would leave the ship, for he did not think it was safe to sail with me among them.

I replied that I owned a good part of the ship, and in that claim, I believed I had a right to speak even further than I had done, and would not be accountable to him or anyone else. He said hardly anything more to me at that time, and I thought the affair had blown over. We were at this time in the Bay of Bengal, and being willing to see the place, I went on shore with the supercargo in the ship's boat to divert myself. Toward evening I was preparing to go on board when one of the men came to me and told me I may as well not trouble myself to come down to the boat, for orders had been given not to carry me on board any more.

It seems that when I went ashore, the boatswain, the gunner, the carpenter, and, in a word, all the inferior officers, told the captain that, as they shipped themselves to serve under his command, they would perform it faithfully, but if I would not quit the ship they would all leave it, and sail no farther with him.

When my nephew, the captain, who came on shore, told me this, I said he should not be concerned by it at all, for I would stay on shore. I only desired he would take care to send me all my necessary things on shore and leave me a sufficient sum of money, and I would find my way to England as well as I could.

So the matter was over in a few hours, the men returned to their duty, and I began to consider what course I should steer.

I was now alone in the most remote part of the world, as I think I may call it, for I was nearly three thousand leagues by sea farther off from England than I was at my island.

Here I had the mortification to see the ship set sail without me. However, my nephew left me two servants, or rather one companion and one servant.

The first was clerk to the purser, whom he engaged to go with me, and the other was his own servant. I took good lodgings in the house of an Englishwoman where several merchants lodged, some French, two Italians, and one Englishman. After a rather long stay, the English merchant who lodged with me made a proposal.

"Countryman," says he, "if you will put one thousand pounds to my one thousand pounds, we will hire a ship here, the first we can get to suit us. You shall be captain, I'll be merchant, and we'll go on a trading voyage to China."

I liked the proposal very well, and the more because it seemed to be expressed with so much goodwill and in so friendly a manner.

In a short time we got a ship we liked well enough. We made this voyage to Achin, in the island of Sumatra, and from thence to Siam, where we exchanged some of our wares for saffron and some arrack: the first a commodity which brings a great price among the Chinese and which, at that time, was much wanted there. In a word, we went up to Suskan, made a very great voyage, were eight months out, and returned to Bengal. I was very well satisfied with my adventure this time.

We next made a voyage to the Spice Islands and

came home in about five months. We sold our spice, which was chiefly cloves and some nutmegs, to the Persian merchants, who carried them away to the gulf; and, making near five to one, we got a great deal of money.

But, to shorten my account, a little while after this there came in a Dutch ship from Batavia. She was a coaster of about two hundred tons burden, and was offered for sale by the captain. Accordingly, we bought the ship and took possession.

When we wished to engage the crew, not one of them was to be found. Afterward I came to know what sort of fellows they were. In short, their history was that this man they called captain was the gunner only, not the commander; that they had been on a trading voyage, in which they had been attacked on shore by some of the Malays, who had killed the captain and three of his men; and that, after the captain was killed, these men, eleven in number, had resolved to run away with the ship, which they did, and brought her to Bengal, leaving the mate and five more men on shore.

We picked up some more English sailors here after this, and some Dutch; and now we resolved on a second voyage to the southeast for cloves and such, that is to say, among the Philippine and Molucca isles. In short, I spent, from first to last, six years in this country, trading from port to port, backward and forward, with very great success, and this was now the last year with my new partner, going in our ship on a voyage to China, but planning first to go to Siam to buy rice.

On this voyage, being by contrary winds obliged to beat up and down a long time in the straits of Malacca and among the islands, we had no sooner cleared those difficult seas than we found our ship had sprung a leak, and we were not able to find out where it was. This forced us to make some port, and my partner, who knew the country better than I did, directed the captain to put into the river of Cambodia (for I had made the English mate, one Mr. Thompson, captain, not being willing to take the charge of the ship upon myself).

While we were here and often going on shore for refreshment there came to me one day an Englishman who was, it seems, a gunner's mate on board an English East India ship which rode in the same river.

"Do you know, sir," said he, "the town of Cambodia lies about fifteen leagues up this river, and there are two large English merchant ships about five leagues on this side, and three Dutch."

"Well," said I, "and what is that to me?"

"This much," he replied, "if you do not put to sea immediately, you will be attacked by five longboats full of men the very next tide and, perhaps, if you are taken, you will be hanged for a pirate, and the particulars be examined afterward. I suppose you know well enough that you were with this ship at Sumatra; that there your captain was murdered by the Malays, with three of his men; and that you, or some of those that were on board with you, ran away with the ship, and are since turned pirates. This is the sum of the story, and you will be seized as pirates, I can assure you, and executed with very little ceremony. If you have any regard for your life and the lives of all your men, put to sea without fail at high water."

After thanking him heartily I went immediately on board and ordered the anchor to be raised, and we sailed out to sea. Then I called my partner into the cabin and told him the story, and we called in the men and they told us the rest of it: but as it took up a great deal of time, before we had done, a seaman came to the cabin door and called out to us that the captain bade him tell us we were being chased.

"Chased!" says I. "By what?"

"By five sloops full of men," says the fellow.

We made ready to fight, but all this while we kept

The Spaniards saw about twenty canoes of Indians
(page 197)

The others shared with the widow and her children
(page 223)

out to sea, the wind with us, and could see the boats at a distance. There were five large longboats following us with all the sail they could make.

Two of these boats (which by our glasses we could see were English) outsailed the rest and were nearly two leagues ahead of the others. They gained upon us till they were near enough for us to call to them with a speaking trumpet which we had on board. So we called to them and bade them come any nearer at their peril.

It was useless. They crowded after us and tried to come under our stern, so we fired our guns at them. This carried away the stern of their last boat.

While this was happening, one of the three boats that was behind, being more forward than the other two, came up to the boat which we had disabled to relieve her, and we could see her take out the men. We called again to the foremost boat, but she crowded close under our stern. Upon this we wore the ship and brought our quarter to bear upon them, and firing three guns more, we found the boat was almost split to pieces. Upon this I immediately manned out our pinnace, with orders to pick up some of the men. Our men in the pinnace followed their orders and took up three men, one of whom was drowning. As soon as they were on board, we crowded all the sail we could, and the boats gave over the chase.

Being thus delivered from danger, I resolved that we should change our course and not let anyone know whither we were going. So we stood out to sea, eastward, quite out of the known course of all European ships.

After a tedious and irregular course, we came within sight of the coast of Cochin China, and resolved to put into a small river to repair a leak. Accordingly, having lightened the ship, we tried to bring her down that we might work on the bottom. The place we were in was wild and barbarous, the people thieves by occupation or profession. They now came all around us with ten or twelve large boats, intending, no doubt, to plunder the ship. Most of our men were at work among the stages, but the handful on board resisted furiously.

An accident gave us a complete victory.

Our carpenter, for the purpose of ship repairs, had two kettles, one filled with boiling pitch and the other with oil, and the man that assisted him had a great iron ladle in his hand. The latter immediately saluted them with a ladleful of the stuff, boiling hot. The carpenter saw it, and himself took a mop and, dipping it in the pitch pot, he and his men threw it among the natives so plentifully that they all ran away howling.

The next day, having repaired our ship of all leaks, we set sail, and in time anchored at the southwest point of the great Gulf of Nanking. There, by the way, I learned by accident that two Dutch ships had gone that length before me, and that I would certainly fall into their hands. I asked the old pilot if there was some creek or small port which I might put into and pursue my business with the Chinese privately, and be in no danger of the enemy. He told me, that if I would sail to the southward about forty-two leagues, there was a little port called Quinchang, where the fathers of the mission usually landed from Macao on their progress to teach the Christian religion to the Chinese, and where no European ships ever put in. We all agreed to go back to this place, and weighed anchor the next day, having only gone twice on shore where we were to get fresh water.

We came to the other port after five days (the wind being contrary), but it was very much to our satisfaction; and I was joyful, and I may say thankful, when I set my foot on shore, resolving, and my partner, too, if it was possible to dispose of ourselves and effects in some way, even though not to our satisfaction every way, we would never set one foot on board that unhappy vessel again.

Both my partner and I had scarce slept a night without dreaming of halters and yardarms. In proportion to our anxiety at sea was our relief now at being on shore; and my partner told me he dreamed he bore a heavy load on his back, which he was to carry up a hill, but the pilot removed it, and the hill sank into the plains. And truly it was so. We were all like men who had been finally freed from a great load.

When we came ashore, the old pilot got us a lodging and a warehouse for our goods. Besides this, he made us acquainted with three missionary priests. One, Father Simon, was appointed, it seems, by order of the chief of the mission to go up to Peking, the royal seat of the Chinese emperor, and only waited for another priest, who was ordered to come to him from Macao, to go along with him. We had scarcely become acquainted before he was inviting me to go on that journey with them.

But we had our ship and our merchandise to dispose of. Providence here began to clear up our way a little. Our old Portuguese pilot brought a Japanese merchant to us, who bought all our saffron and gave us a very good price for it. I proposed to him to deal with us for our ship also, and he consented to hire her to go to Japan, saying that on his return he would buy the ship. So away he went to Japan.

The priest for whom Father Simon was waiting arrived about this time, so there was nothing now to prevent our setting out for Peking.

CHAPTER FIFTEEN
ADVENTURES ASHORE

e were twenty-five days getting to Peking through a country infinitely populous, but I think badly cultivated. The husbandry, the economy, and the way of living was miserable, though they boast so much of the industry of the people. The pride of the people is infinitely great; their ostentation is inexpressible; and, if they can, they love to keep multitudes of servants or slaves. For example, passing the house of a country gentleman, we saw him, a perfect Don Quixote in pomp and plentitude, dining in his garden.

He sat under a tree, lolling about in a great elbow chair, his meat being brought to him by two women slaves. Another fed the squire with a spoon, and yet a fourth held the dish with one hand, and with the other scraped off what the former let fall upon his worship's beard and taffety vest.

At length we arrived at Peking. I had nobody with me but the youth whom my nephew, the captain, had sent to attend me as a servant, and who proved very trusty and diligent; and my partner had nobody with him but one servant, who was a kinsman. As for the Portuguese pilot, he being desirous to see the world, we bore his charges for his company and to use him as an interpreter, for he understood the language of the country and spoke good French and a little English; and, indeed, this old man was most useful to us everywhere, for we had not been more than a week at Peking when he came laughing, and told us there was a great caravan of Muscovite, or Russian and Polish merchants preparing to set out on their journey by land to Moscow, within four or five weeks.

It was in the beginning of February when we set out from Peking. The company was very large, and, as near as I can remember, came to between three and four hundred horses and upwards of one hundred and twenty men, very well armed, and prepared for all events. The road at times passed through districts where the chief industry was tempering the earth for chinaware. I was shown a house built, as we call it in England, with lath and plaster, but all the plastering was chinaware. The people tell you incredible tales of accomplishment in this line. One yarn was of a ship made of earthenware, big enough to carry fifty men, with all its masts and sails. I thought that the narrator lied, so I smiled and said nothing.

In two days we passed the great China wall made for a fortification against the barbarians. Here I began to understand the necessity for keeping together in a caravan as we moved around, for we saw several troops of Tartars roving about. However when I came to see them clearly, I wondered very much how the Chinese Empire could be conquered by such fellows, for they are very wild in nature keeping no order, and understanding no discipline and fighting without any set rules.

We were all this while in the Chinese dominions, and therefore the Tartars were not so bold as afterward; but in about five days we entered a vast, wild desert, which took us three days and nights' march; and we were obliged to carry our water with us in great leathern bottles, and to encamp all night, just as I have heard they do in the desert of Arabia.

I asked our guides whose dominion this was in, and they told me this was a kind of border area which might be called No Man's Land. For, although it was a part of Great Karakathay, or Grand Tartary, it was still all reckoned to belong to China, but there was no care taken here to preserve it from the inroads of thieves, and therefore it was reckoned the worst desert in the whole march, though we were to go over some much larger.

We went on nearly a month after this, the roads not being as good as at first, though still in the dominions of the emperor of China. They lay for the most part in villages, some of which were fortified because of the constant incursions of the Tartars.

At last we came to the city of Naun, or Naum.

After this we passed several great rivers and two dreadful deserts, one of which we were sixteen days getting across. On the 13th of April we came to the frontiers of the Muscovite, or Russian, dominions. As we advanced into them, we were very much obliged to the care the Czar of Muscovy had taken to have cities and towns built in as many places as it is possible to place them. Here his soldiers kept garrison, something like the stationary soldiers placed by the Romans in the remotest countries of their empire. Nonetheless, wherever we came, though at these towns and stations the garrisons and governors were Russians and professed Christians, the inhabitants were mere pagans, sacrificing to idols and praying to the sun, moon, and stars, or all the host of heaven.

In a village near Nertzinskay, I had the curiosity to go and see their way of living, which is most brutish and insufferable. They had, I suppose, had a great sacrifice that day, for there stood upon the old stump of a tree, an idol made of wood, frightful as the devil, at least, as anything we can think of to represent the devil can be made. It had a head not at all resembling any creature that the world ever saw; ears as big as goats' horns, and as high; eyes as big as a crown piece; a nose like a crooked ram's horn, and a mouth extended four-cornered, like that of a lion, with horrible teeth, hooked like a parrot's under a bill. It was dressed up in the filthiest manner that you could suppose: its upper garment was of sheepskins, with the wool outward; a great Tartar bonnet was on the head, with two horns growing through it. It was about eight feet high, yet had no feet or legs, nor any other human parts.

This scarecrow was set up at the other side of the village, and when I came near it, there were sixteen or seventeen creatures, all lying flat upon the ground round this formidable block of shapeless wood. A little way off from the idol, and at the door of a tent or hut made entirely of dried sheepskins and cowskins, stood three butchers (I thought they were such). When I came nearer to them, I found they had long knives in their hands, and in the middle of the tent there appeared three dead sheep and one young bullock or steer lying on a sacrificial table.

These, it seems, were sacrifices to that senseless log of an idol. The three men were priests belonging to it, and the seventeen prostrated wretches were the people who brought the offering and were making their prayers to that stock.

I confess I was more moved and bothered at their worship of a hobgoblin than ever I was at anything in my life. I rode up to the image or monster, call it what you will, and with my sword, made a stroke at the bonnet that was on its head and cut it in two; and one of our men who was with me took hold of the sheepskin that covered it and pulled at it. At this, a most hideous outcry and howling ran throughout the village, and two or three hundred people came about my ears, so that I was glad to make a run for it, for we saw some had bows and arrows; but I resolved from that moment to visit them again.

Our caravan rested three nights at the town, which was about four miles off, in order to provide some horses which they wanted, several of the horses having been lamed and jaded with the badness of the way and the long march over the last desert. So we had some leisure here to put my plan into execution. I communicated my project to a Scots merchant in Moscow. I told him, if I could get but four or five well-armed men to go with me, I was resolved to go and destroy that vile, abominable idol, and let the people see that it had no power to help itself, and consequently could not be an object of worship, or to be prayed to, much less help them that offered sacrifices to it.

He laughed at me at first, but finding me resolute, he consented to join me, and he insisted upon bringing a stout fellow, one of his countrymen, as an ally.

He brought me a Tartar's robe of sheepskins and a bonnet, along with a bow and arrows, and provided the same for himself and his countrymen, so that if the people saw us, they would not be able to determine who we were.

All the next night we spent in mixing up some combustible matter with aqua vitae, gunpowder, and such other materials as we could get; and, carrying a good quantity of tar in a little pot, we set out upon our expedition about an hour after nightfall.

We came to the place about eleven o'clock at night, and in the great hut where we had seen the three priests whom we had mistaken for butchers, we saw a light; and going up close to the door, we heard what sounded like five or six people talking.

We determined on making them our prisoners,

and tying their hands, compelled them to stand and see their idols destroyed, which we accomplished by means of the combustibles we had brought with us.

We appeared in the morning among our fellows, who were busy getting ready for our journey, and no one could suggest that we have been anywhere but in our beds, as wayfarers are all supposed to be to fit themselves for the fatigues of the day's journey.

But the affair did not end there. The next day a great number of the country people came to the town gates, and in a most outraged manner demanded satisfaction of the Russian governor for the insult to their priests, and the burning of their idol. The Russian governor spoke with all the good words imaginable, and at last, to appease them, told them that a caravan had left for Russia that morning, and perhaps it was some of them who had done them this injury, and that he would send after them to inquire into it. Then the governor sent after us, intimating that if any in our caravan had done it, they should make their escape, and that, whether we had done it or not, we should make all possible haste.

The captain of the caravan took the hint, and we went forward two days and two nights without any long stop, and then we put up at a village called Plothus. Thence we hastened on towards Jarawena, but on the second day's march from Plothus, clouds of dust behind us at a great distance made some of our people notice that we were being pursued. The third day, Tartars came pouring in upon us toward the dusk of the evening. They did not come on us like thieves, as we expected, but sent three messengers to us to demand the men to be delivered to them who had abused their priests and burned their god Cham Chi-Thaungu with fire, that they might burn them with fire. If we agreed, they said they would go away and do us no further harm. Otherwise they would destroy us all.

The leader of the caravan sent word he was quite certain that it was not done by any of our camp. They were far from being satisfied with this for an answer, and we escaped them only through the cunning of a Cossack of Jarawena, who rode away from our rear, and taking a great circuit, came on the army of the Tartars, as if he had been sent to find them, and told them that the people who had burned the Cham Chi-Thaungu had gone to Sibeilka with a caravan of miscreants, as he called them, that is to say, Christians, and that they had resolved to burn the god Schal-Isarg, which belonged to the Tongueses.

Upon this, the Tartars went away in a great hurry,

and in less than three hours, they were entirely out of sight. So we passed safely on to Jarawena, and thence through a frightful desert to a country pretty well inhabited.

I have nothing material to say of my own affairs till I came to Tobolski, the capital city of Siberia, where I let the caravan go and made provision for the winter.

This being the country where the state criminals of Russia are all banished, the city was full of noblemen, princes and gentlemen, with several of whom I became friendly.

About the latter end of May I began to pack up, but it was not until the beginning of June that I left this remote place, a city so far off the trade routes that I know now how it could ever be much talked of.

We arrived safe at Archangel on the 18th of July, but were obliged to stay at this place six weeks for the arrival of the ships.

We set sail from Archangel on the 20th of August, in a German ship the same year; and after an uneventful voyage, arrived safe in the Elbe River on the 18th of September. Here my partner and I made a very good sale of our goods. On dividing the profit, my share amounted to three thousand four hundred and seventy-five pounds, seventeen shillings and

three pence, including about six hundred pounds'
worth of diamonds which I purchased at Bengal.

To conclude, having stayed nearly four months in
Hamburg, I journeyed from there by land to The
Hague, where I embarked in the regular packet and
arrived in London on the 10th of January, 1705,
having been absent from England ten years and nine
months. And here I am, preparing for a longer
journey than all these, having lived a life of infinite
variety for seventy-two years, and learned enough to
know the value of retirement and the blessing of
ending our days in peace.

Friday cried out they were going to shoot (page 228)

There stood an idol made of wood (page 248)